HOPING, COPING & MOPING

RONNA JEVNE, PH.D.

HEALTH INFORMATION PRESS
Los Angeles, California 90010

Library of Congress Cataloging-in-Publication Data

Jevne, Ronna Fay.
    Hoping, coping & moping : handling life when illness makes it tough /
    Ronna Jevne.
        p. cm.
    Includes bibliographical references
    ISBN #1-885987-20-X
        1. Sick--Psychology--Anecdotes. 2. Adjustment (psychology)--Anecdotes.

    R726.5 .J478 2000
    155.9'3--dc21   00-026716

Health Information Press
4727 Wilshire Blvd., Suite 300
Los Angeles, California 90010 U.S.A.
1-800-MED-SHOP

http://hipbooks.com/

Printed in the United States of America

This book is dedicated to Allen, with whom I share

meaning in the difficult

fun in the serious

delight in the unexpected

and

joy in the everyday

&

to Jack,

who laughs in the face of fate

opens his heart to the hurting

and

hopes in the face of pain.

Acknowledgements

*N*o book is ever authored by one person. It is a lifetime of encounters that contribute to what we bring to the written page. For each experience and relationship that has challenged, coaxed and cajoled me into saying a heartier "yes" to life, I am grateful.

A special acknowledgment to Donna Reilly Williams, herself an author and veteran of managing chronic illness, for her encouragement, contributions and effort toward this book. Thank you also to Karen Westra for the library research; to the staff and volunteers of Hope House for keeping the writing uncluttered with academic diversions; to Wendy Edey and Mufty Mathewson for their reading of drafts and for their lightness of heart. And finally, to Shelly Bernard, a special thank you for her positive approach to editing and to finishing the final details.

The perspectives offered and many of the stories told in *Hoping, Coping and Moping* come from my life and from Donna's. A few have been told to me. Without them, there would be no book. For the most part they are shared in such a way that I hope you could say, "This could happen in my life, or in the life of someone I know."

Contents

Introduction

Hope is the art of living.[1]

*In the heart of each of us, there is a voice, a small voice that
yearns to say "yes" to life. If nurtured and strengthened, it invites,
encourages, pulls, pushes, cajoles and seduces us to go forward.
Whether viewed as a human need, a biological life force,
a mental perspective or an eternal pull to transcend self,
hope is capable of changing lives.*[2]

*S*ometimes hope lends a hand. Sometimes it needs a hand. Sooner or
later life introduces us vividly to our need for hope. Although familiar
with hope from previous experiences, this book began on June 29, 1997.

Allen, my husband and the most special guy in the world to me, was
five weeks out of a surgery that nearly took his life. It was supposed to be
a simple surgery. He was to have been home in under a week.

Everything went wrong. Initially he wouldn't stop bleeding. He ended
up with three surgeries in four days. Each brought a further complication.
His kidneys failed. His lungs gave out. He had a small heart attack. There
were 8 uncertain days in intensive care. His ultimate recovery was in no
small part due to the exemplary dedication of his physician and the staff.
With good care, and good luck, he was home recovering in a month. On
this particular Sunday afternoon, he just could not get comfortable as he
attempted the post-operative shuffle that follows surgery and precedes full

recovery. The pain was getting the best of him despite his medication and his naturally optimistic nature. Finally he succumbed to the recliner. I made a fresh pot of coffee. I got out the chocolate ice cream and scooped an overdose portion into a dessert dish offering it to him as a servant who was knowingly powerless to do much else. What else would help? What other ways are there to handle life when illness makes it tough? Could we "light a candle" rather than "curse the darkness"? And the book was born.

Some days being sick is

    just plain difficult,

        boring,

            distressing,

                and frustrating.

Even frightening.

For two decades as a health psychologist, I have watched people beat the odds. They live longer and more fully than their medical charts would suggest is possible. Science has been playing catch up in an effort to explain how that can be and whether it can be learned. A whole field of health research called "psychoneuroimmunology" has emerged to uncover mysteries of the mind-body relationship.

This research provides us with evidence of what folk wisdom has taught for generations: how we feel, what we think and how we behave influence our health. To what degrees and in exactly which ways they are related are still unfolding. We are still discovering what combination of body, soul and surroundings contribute to our well being. It is not as simple as "mind over matter" or "positive thinking." To suggest that it is that simple would be to suggest we have control over everything. We do not. Many little daily decisions and actions are necessary if we are to have the greatest possible well being.

Few people find they are at their best when they are nauseated, in pain and facing uncertainty. When illness persists, it gets harder. Our hope wanes. We are tempted to believe we are victims of the condition. However, when medicine reaches its limits, we may not have reached ours. The task of health care professionals is to keep searching for possible alternatives to relieve or cure our condition. Doing what we can each day to feel even a bit better is our part.

Holding on to our hope when the situation isn't great is a task that needs intentional effort at times. Hope is the voice inside that whispers "yes, you can." Keeping hopelessness out of the situation is key to doing what is possible and enjoying life while we wait for and contribute to whatever good may come tomorrow.

Three serious conditions and a poor prognosis are enough to bring doubt to the hardiest of souls. Jack had fought a lymphoma that should have taken his life. The polymyalgic rheumatica, the rheumatoid arthritis and the osteoporosis further complicated his life. His pain load was intense. He nearly gave up. Instead, as he put it, "I finally realized I had to get involved in my own recovery." Jack claims that it was hanging onto hope that made the difference. I am often reminded of his words when my challenges seem endless:

I had to build that barrier between hope and hopelessness. It is very easy when you are suffering all the time to give up—for an hour, a day, a minute. And it is pretty easy to blame others, too. But

it's you who must build that wall between hope and hopelessness.
There's always hope. But sometimes you have to work at it.

A decade later, Jack is still involved as the founding father of the Hope Foundation of Alberta, a non-profit organization affiliated with the University of Alberta that is dedicated to studying and enhancing hope in people facing adversity, particularly those suffering serious illness and pain.

This book is not about documenting new findings in the science of getting well. It will comment on scientific understandings from time to time, most often in an annotation at the end of the book. This is not a therapy book or a recipe to feel good. It is simply a collection of suggestions I and others have found helpful. Adopt some, ignore some, change and personalize others. See if they fit for you.

There is no panacea. There is no recipe. We hope. We cope. And on occasion, we mope. We probably need to do all three. Hoping and coping are like twins. They have even been referred to as the *ping* twins: ho-ping and co-ping.[3] Despite their resemblance they have their unique features. *Hoping* keeps our sights set on confidently expecting a good future. *Coping* helps us deal with the practical and realistic day-to-day challenges. Both are important. Both influence each other. If we have no hope, we see little point to coping. If we are consistently not coping, hoping will soon be on a slippery slope. Finally, *moping* is our time out. It lets us moan and groan and grieve and despair the lost dreams. It empties the bucket of "poor me's" to make room for "new me's." Overdone, it can become an unhelpful rut. Totally ignored, it may weave a web of unspoken pain that has no place to go.

I don't wish to suggest that you just wave a magic wand and become the epitome of optimism under dire circumstances. It is possible, though, to make a decision to make things a little better; to do what is within one's control. Sometimes that means making an effort many times a day. Some days a good day could be just holding your own. A day of moping isn't a day of weakness or failure. It may even help get the emotional and mental sludge out of your system.

Hoping, Coping and Moping offers suggestions that acknowledge our need to do some of each. Some ideas may help in the short run; some in the long run. Some things may work one day but not the next. Some things are easy to implement; others require thought and courage. Others are just "not you." For each of us, our thoughts about life, about illness, about ourselves and about others shape our experience of an illness. Each of us has our own style. Some people will agree with your choices. Others won't. So be it! Your sole purpose in life is not to comply with other's expectations. Whether you are reading this book as you recover from the flu or in the last days of your life, I hope it provides thoughts and smiles. It might also bring a tear or two. That's healthy, too.

All we ever have is the present moment. If you can string together enough good moments, first thing you know the situation is taking on that "new light." Regret for the past or concern for the future can contribute to distress in the present. What each of us has today is now. Whether you use one or many of the ideas presented here, today is a good day to experiment with taking charge of your hope. Tomorrow will be here soon enough.

Hoping, Coping and Moping is deliberately written with minimal jargon, imperfect grammar, occasionally with humor and without apology for its directness. At the end of each section, I suggest you stop and reflect on the questions provided. Maybe even ask someone you trust to discuss them with you.

Thinking is as important as reading. However, thinking and reading are not a substitute for practicing. Suggestions for further reading are offered in the "Recommended Reading" and "Notes" sections. This book may raise questions and generate feelings. Considering those questions and dealing with the feelings is hard work. Accept that you need to take steps at your own pace. I sincerely hope you have someone who will walk with you along this difficult path and who will celebrate each step with you.

P.S. If you need or prefer to be cranky rather than hopeful right now, put this book down. You have every right to feel the way you do. If you are a committed pessimist, feel free to avoid any of these suggestions, as they do have the potential to contribute to feeling better, at least briefly.

Attitude

Getting it in perspective

*Everything can be taken from a man but one thing: the last of the
human freedoms—to choose one's attitude in any given set of
circumstances, to choose one's own way.[4]*
—Viktor Frankl

You hear it all the time: "He has a great attitude." "She is remarkable." There are those people who have a handle on life. They have it in perspective. In other words, they have found a way to live in the world that accommodates their situation.

Your perspective is your outlook, your attitude towards a situation. And attitude is a very powerful force. If you have a crummy attitude, you will probably have a crummy life.

Life doesn't come ready-made. There are no instructions that say, "Just peel the label back and let cook for thirty minutes. Serve with packaged seasonings." We have a role to play in our own destiny. To the degree we can, we move towards satisfying experiences. No one starts out in life thinking, "When I grow up I wanna' be ill." But it happens, and then we have to deal with it as best we can. The world has beauty and ugliness, logic and craziness, sickness and health. People suffer. Some die. We are not here forever. While I may have little choice over the suffering I endure, I have a good deal of choice over how I endure it.

Changing or adapting our perspective isn't easy, especially when pain gets in the way. Letting go of the way things ought to have been means grieving for a future that may not be, while gently and consistently creating a new perspective on how things presently are.

Remember, you still have choices.

Abdicate from the role of the perfect patient

Perfectionism is slow death at the best of times. Trying to be the perfect patient takes a great deal of effort. If you read each of the suggestions in this book and add them to your "I have to do perfectly" list, you have missed the point.

What's a perfect patient? Here is one person's description:

The perfect sick person is patient, knowledgeable, accepts her illness, has a sense of humor, uses relaxation to kill the pain, is kind to all advice-givers, is thankful for all gifts, is pleased with all visitors and hides it well in the rare cases when this is not true, follows the prescribed diet, gets as much exercise as possible, runs a support group for fellow sufferers, invites children onto the bed and reads to them, writes an inspirational autobiography, and never soils a clean set of sheets.[5]

Do you really want to try to live up to that ideal?

Refuse to apologize

How many times have you said, "I'm sorry"? In one way or another, have you been conveying, "I'm sorry I can't walk faster. I'm sorry I can't eat this. I'm sorry I can't bring in the income I used to. I am sorry our social life has changed. I'm sorry my condition taxes you. I am sorry I don't have the energy to go to the ball game"?

Our culture programs us to value success, independence and popularity; not our ability to be ill. If we are not these things, we feel shame.[6] But being ill is not something we need to be ashamed of. You didn't ask for the condition you have. No one starts out in life thinking, "When I grow up, I think I'll be ill." For that matter, no one marries for the purpose of divorcing or learns to drive believing they will be injured in a car accident. You are not less of a person because you are have a health condition. Perhaps you are different because of the illness. Perhaps your life and even the life of those you love has changed. That's what illness usually does, at least for a period of time. It changes things.

If you could say something other than "I am sorry" to someone whose life is affected by your condition, in whatever small or large way, what would you say instead? Try this. Say out loud: "I am not less of a person because I am ill. I acknowledge our lives are different. I, however, am also a worthwhile person." Did it feel true? If you can't say it out loud, can you begin by saying it inside?

We live in a society that values youth, health and productivity. "I'm sorry" is a way of saying, "I am less because I can't..." Because you can't does not mean you are less, it just means that you are different. Coming to terms with being different is a tough task. It is also key to feeling some hope for the future. As one person said, "Hope is not about everything turning out okay. It is about being okay however things turn out."

Remind yourself of your value.
Be specific.

How?

Every way you can think of:

A fridge magnet.

A book mark.

A little reminder in your wallet.

A bedtime meditation.

Write it down, again and again and again. Read it over and over and over.

Just get started.

Are you struggling? Are you saying inside, "Saying sorry is a way of being courteous"? Even if you are right, isn't there another a way of doing it more constructively? Could you say, "I have special needs. Can the situation accommodate my needs?" Could you say, "My circumstances are such that I will need help with..."?

If you look down on yourself, so will others.

"Despair is down. Hope is up."[7]

Expect a miracle.
Believe in exceptions.

The naysayers of the world believed humans would never fly, automobiles would never replace the horse-drawn carriage and no one would ever walk on the moon. Great athletes have been born of physical limits, and inventions arise out of necessity. Who truly knows what is possible?

In a world dominated by science, hope has taken on a mathematical quality. Your chances of recovery are statistical. The odds may be fifty-fifty, or 95 to 1. The probability of this or that happening is a number calculated on the basis of large groups of people.

However, you are an individual. You have a unique body, unique memories, and unique thoughts. You have your own set of friends, eccentric or conventional as some of them might be. No one can know how you are going to do. Why assume you would be average or, even worse, less than average? There is no prescription for who will become the exception. There is growing evidence that biology is not destiny.

Some dear soul sooner or later will give you the "mustn't have false hopes" lecture. Tell them you really appreciate their concern but that you have found false despair equally unhelpful. Of the two, you prefer to err on the side of possibility. At the Hope Foundation, we talk with many people who face insurmountable odds.[8] In our experience at Hope House, the wonderful old renovated building on the University of Alberta campus that serves as the home of the Foundation, we have come to define false hope as that part of your hope that others don't share.[9]

Spontaneous remission is the scientific name for unexplained recoveries. Call them miracles. Call them hard work. Call them luck. Whatever you call them, write Brandon O'Regan and Caryle Hirshberg in *Spontaneous Remissions: An Annotated Bibliography*, "there is a wide body of evidence suggesting that extraordinary healing, including regression of normally fatal tumors, takes place with no known scientific explanation."[10]

Every one of us knows an "against the odds" story. You could be one. There is no guarantee you will be. The odds may even be unlikely that you will be. But you certainly are unlikely to be if you are not even open to the possibility.

Not all remarkable recoveries are overnight miracles. Twenty years ago, Donna was diagnosed with colitis, an often frustrating, painful and progressive condition. Told that it would never go away, she was advised to accommodate a new and limited lifestyle. Sufficiently confident to consider that physicians are not always visionaries, Donna opted for a concerted effort at wellness. Taking charge of the choices about her own care, gleaning from what each specialist could offer, she chose a multi-faceted holistic protocol. Colitis-free for years now, she doesn't try to define why it happened. She is content to accept that miracles come wrapped in various forms.

It's only impossible until it happens.

Believe science is working on it

When I was working as a psychologist in a cancer hospital, I was often surprised to receive visits from patients years after they had been sent home to die. This happened more times than I can accurately recall. There was something heartwarming about their dropping by just to say "hello" when they came to visit a friend or family member who was undergoing in-hospital treatment.

There are many cases of unexplained recovery. They are well documented and no one doubts their validity. However, at the same time no one knows how they happen. Lewis Thomas has referred to this mystery as a "solid basis for hope."[11] In some cases, science does come up with the answer to life threatening illnesses.

Look back over one decade: your neighbor may have a transplanted heart; Uncle Fred takes pills that lower his blood pressure; George was diagnosed with the use of an MRI early enough to save his life; a child in Jimmy's class had a bone marrow transplant and is well enough to ride his bike across your lawn again; microsurgery saved your friend's eyesight; polio is virtually gone, as is tuberculosis.[12,13]

Yes, we still have AIDS. And Lou Gehrig's disease is still progressive. There are increasing numbers of cases of tuberculosis again, and cancer is still a dreaded word. "Superbugs" are developing that are resistant to antibiotics. But, you have a choice: you can despair that the future may not be as creative as the past, or you can focus on the potential for intervention.

The big hope is, of course, that science will discover the magic bullet solution for *your* condition. In the interim, some remarkable things are happening. There is no denying that the lives of many are helped in a variety of ways, even in the absence of a full cure. Persons with arthritis have some assistance with pain. Diabetics can live full lives. Science is at the threshold of providing symptomatic relief for Parkinson's patients. Dedicated teams of people are working in laboratories and clinics towards breakthroughs in many conditions. Even if yours is a condition that is not particularly well funded, solutions and help come from the most unusual places. Offshoots of research, sometimes unrelated to health, generate new possibilities. We have walked on the moon and visited Mars. If these things are possible, so is the discovery of cures for cerebral palsy, diabetes and spinal cord injury. It is human nature to search for solutions. Dedicated creative men and women are at work at this very minute.

There is reason to hope.

Someone is worse off

There is nothing wrong with feeling sorry for yourself. It's easy to have a pity party. Staying at the party too long isn't healthy, though. You will lose friends, your symptoms will bother you more, and depression will set in. Although a variety of factors contribute to depression, your moping muscle is one that you don't want to over exercise.

It is easy to notice everyone who has more mobility, more resources, more whatever. It seems to be a human trait to do so. There will always be someone more fortunate than you. You don't have to be ill to catch yourself noticing that you want part of someone else's life. It may even be important to do so in order to come to terms with your situation. Seldom, though, are we taught to look at those who are less fortunate than we are. That may be equally important in order to develop that much-needed perspective that prevents us from feeling like a victim. The following observations were made by two different patients.

    ❧   *When I first had to be on a very restrictive diet, my first*
            Christmas was hard. No goodies. No gravy. No potatoes.
            No bread. I had never had to be disciplined about food but
            I made it through the festive season with flying colors. The
            example and words of a special friend made the difference.
            At 78, he had for years been fasting one day a month in
            respect for those who hungered across the world. He
            pointed out that what I was eating was a feast in many
            countries. I had been concentrating on what I could not eat

rather than on what I could eat; on what I couldn't do rather than on what I could do.

❦   *My husband and I were in Africa and had taken some food to a widow in the countryside. Stricken with polio as a child, this woman could only crawl and had no family. She lived in a small hut made of reeds with a dirt floor. When we bent down to crawl through the doorway, the three of us pretty well filled the interior space. Expressing the gratitude for the food we had brought her, this woman asked if she could pray for us. There in the midst of abject poverty I was almost overwhelmed by her belief that she had something to give us.*

Think about what would make the situation worse

❧ *Three weeks after surgery, Carol hit the doldrums when biopsies showed that her case of Crohn's disease was back. It took her a couple of days before she could say, "But I don't have cancer." It could have been worse.*

❧ *My mom died of complications of open heart surgery. I think often of the father of a friend of mine who also had bypass surgery the same month. He lingered for eleven years, totally paralyzed from a reaction to a drug that was meant only to relax him. Losing Mom was hard, but it could have been worse.*

❧ *Elaine shuffled down the hospital corridor trying not to feel sorry for herself. She had not had a visitor for several days. She was lonely and wishing a friend would come by. No particular friend. Just a friend. One of the drawbacks of being single was not having a special someone to care for her.*

Then she passed by another patient's room, and Elaine realized things could be worse. The woman looked so ill. The two little ones were obviously preschool-aged and very unkempt. Their little noses needed wiping. A man was yelling at the lady in the bed, "You bitch! You did this on purpose. You are going to go and die and leave me with them!" and he pointed at the children, as if they had no

15

names. Yes, things could be worse than having busy friends.

❧ *It was a hard winter. I had major surgery months before, and yet the pain persisted. The exploratory surgery I just underwent was to see if they had missed a tumor. My husband and I were nervous. Thankfully, the doctor came by soon after I was conscious. No tumor!*

Only a curtain separated us from the young couple awaiting their news. We heard their doctor say, "I'm sorry," and the sobbing began. It could have been us. It could have been worse.

Ask yourself, would you trade?

It was the strangest 24 hours of my sabbatical. During my year of exploring hope, I had the privilege of talking with an assortment of people about the concept and phenomenon of hope in their lives. One evening, crowded in our comfortable fireside rumpus room and surrounded by oak shelves overstocked with books, a group of women spoke to me of their experiences with cancer. They spoke of the delays in diagnosis, the disfigurement from the surgery, their fears of reoccurrence. Most of all, most passionately, they spoke of being treated as numbers, of sitting in line-ups, of being part of research protocols where even the doctor didn't know if they were receiving treatment. Yes, they hoped for survival. Yes, they hoped to be free from pain. But most of all they hoped to be seen as a person. When they discovered I would be talking with female inmates the next day, their response was, "at least we have our freedom."

Twelve hours later in the barrenness of a linoleum-tiled room, the women at the remand center hesitantly began to share their experiences. They spoke of the endless waiting, the deliberate stripping of identity and the hurdles to communication. They hoped to "beat the charge," they hoped for reduced sentences, they hoped for contact with people they believed cared. Most of all they hoped to be treated like they were more than garbage—"like a person who still has feelings." Sharing with them that the previous evening I had spoken to women with cancer, their unsolicited and compassionate response was, "Wow, at least we have our health."

Consider the possibility that suffering is part of life

This is a world of suffering. No matter who you are,
you are either threatened with suffering, or actually subject
to it. You have been stricken or you know that you will be.
—E. De Pressensé[14]

Suffering is built right into life. No one escapes. Some seemingly get a disproportionate share. In our culture we have a need for people not to visibly suffer. We want suffering fixed or, at least, out of our sight. Our efforts to avoid suffering are easy to observe. Painkillers, cosmetics, fluoride toothpaste and aisles of supplements are part of the illusion of our immunity to pain, ugliness, deterioration and illness. Emphasis on youth, health and employment help us to sustain the illusion. Yet, we all know someone for whom the dream was broken.

For example, there was one young couple, both with their master's degrees. A week after the husband's convocation, the wife was in unanticipated brain surgery. The week after that, she was fighting for her life because of a subsequent stroke. In the months following, she was still fighting to be seen, not only as a patient, but also as a person—a person now without her mobility, with half her sight and without the face she had known.

Or, consider the dynamic architect who fell while inspecting a building site. He regained consciousness ten days later not knowing who the people who stood by his bedside were, not even knowing the name by which he was addressed.

Then there was the elderly couple who enjoyed good health in retirement whose lives were forever altered because of a drunk driver. And certainly, tragedy should only strike once. The husband who is the joy and center of a young woman's life shouldn't die of cancer. Not when she herself suffers a life threatening condition and must have risky, life-saving surgeries.

Suffering is something that is supposed to happen to someone else. Our hopes will be fulfilled. Someone else will do the suffering.

We see suffering on the late night news. It is possible to watch an entire war on television. But we are allowed not to feel it. We can finish a pizza while we hear of the genocide in Africa. There is ample time to retrieve a Coke during a commercial. Media protects us. Tragedy is performed and completed within 30 second bites, followed by the local weather. It is not supposed to happen off the screen, not in our life. It is supposed to happen to someone else.

But in fact, suffering is part of life. Few are fortunate enough to be exempt.

Recognize that your suffering is unique to you

Suffering, no matter how multiplied, is always individual.
—*Lorraine Dahlberg*[15]

Suffering is universal and yet it is very individual. For the most part, the suffering we live is the suffering we understand. If the worst thing that has happened to you is a fender-bender involving your Mercedes, or a stain on our ultra-suede suit, you have little understanding for the parents whose son is dying of AIDS or the businessman who has been relegated to the status of mail clerk after a brain injury. It isn't necessary to be in the way of flowing lava to know the experience of fear, to be paralyzed by a drunk driver to know rage, or to bury three children following the randomness of a tornado to know despair. But the *knowing* in each of these cases is different.

The stories that unveil our suffering are unique to us. What we suffer from will depend on our culture and on the family in which we were raised.

One young woman kept shaking her head as she intensely pleaded with me to understand, "I am Italian. I am Italian! Italians don't go on welfare. I have to find a way to support my son." In her culture and in her family, this was an edict. No matter what my interpretation might be, if she could not find work, then her suffering would be shame. For others, suffering may be the anguish of aloneness, the torment of failure or the dependency imposed by illness.

What is your particular suffering? Your suffering is not synonymous to your condition. The condition brings loss and limits. What have you lost? What are you losing? What are the impinging limits that cause your suffering?

Until we know from what we suffer, we may be spending energy and time on the wrong issue. If you suffer from pain, of course you want relief. If the pain means you cannot shop for yourself, you have the possible suffering of feeling dependent or isolated as well. Those sufferings, too, deserve your attention. To get your situation in perspective, ask yourself, "From what do I suffer?" When you can answer that, then you can forgive people for not understanding and you can avoid making your suffering the "mother of all sufferings." Most importantly, you will be able to address the real issue.

Shift from "why?" to "what now?"

Some individuals have no need to know how they developed their conditions. Others are puzzled, wondering why this would occur to them. And finally there are others, like the patient who said to me: "I was abandoned when I was three. I am sure it all began with that loneliness," who are convinced that they themselves have contributed to the onset of the illness.

You need to do what works for you. If it helps you to believe you have your condition for a reason, great. If it helps to believe you were given the disease to learn a specific lesson, okay. If it helps to see a psychotherapist and explore your early childhood looking for the event(s) that might have been the seed of your illness, fine.

It is important to know "why" only if knowing so in some way contributes to making your situation more tolerable. It is natural to want to make sense of the events of our lives, but it isn't always necessary to do so to move on with life.

On the other hand, if you are plagued with wondering, "Why me? Why now?" give the other perspective a thought. Maybe life just *is*. Maybe some things just *are*. Maybe some things are not explainable. Illness is complex. Misfortune cannot always be explained. You could simply have been in the wrong place at the wrong time. The bottom line is you can't know whether your lifestyle choices, a traumatic event, or genetics are the basis of your condition. If your mom and dad both died of heart disease before they were 50, your chance of getting heart disease was unquestionably higher. Living a stressed life, smoking and being overweight contribute as well. It isn't always clear cut "why" something happens, especially when there could be more than one reason.

If you had an answer to "why," then what would you be able to move on with in your life? Why not move on now? Take at least some of the energy you are using to figure out "why" and apply it to creating meaning in your life, *now*. Maybe the challenge is not to figure out some hidden meaning of your illness, but to make meaning out of what you have been dealt. Only you can know how long you want to spend on "why" and when you would like to switch to "what now?"

Notice how you explain things

We all have day-to-day variations in how we see things. There will, though, be somewhat of a pattern.

Are you more like the person who says:

    It's awful. It will never end.

        Everything is wrong.

            This will ruin my whole life.

        And it's all my fault.

    There is nothing I can do.

Or are you like the person who says:

    It's tough, but it won't last forever.

        My hips are bad, but my feet are still okay.

            It may mean I have to change work.

        It certainly is bad luck.

    Somehow I will manage.

        Of the two, who do you expect will have the greater quality of life?

24

Experiment with how you explain things

Martin Seligman has been studying optimism for years. He and others leave little doubt that there are health benefits to being an optimist.[16-22] A characteristic of optimists is how they explain their situations. Despite the facts of a situation, optimists tend to see more possibilities. They are more hopeful. Try this exercise.

Describe your situation:

- As if it is permanent; as if nothing about it could ever change,
- As if it is universal, affecting everything about your life,
- As if it is completely your fault,
- As if there is nothing you can do about it.

Then describe your situation:

- As if it is temporary; something about it will change,
- As if it affects only part of your life and not others,
- As if you are not totally responsible for it,
- As if you are able to influence parts of it.

Can you feel the difference?

We have more than one voice in our head. You might think of them as two attorneys, one presenting evidence for "life is awful" and one for "life is wonderful." You can rule out any evidence you want. You are the judge. Your decision is final.[23]

Ask why <u>not</u> me?

Why me? Why not someone else?

Is there any particular reason why you would be selected to be exempt from the trials and tribulations of life? Did you somehow fall into the trap of believing that if you led a certain kind of life you would not become ill? Or that if you did, you have failed some undefined life-test?

Which of the following apply to you?

I shouldn't be ill because:

- I was always health conscious.
- I am a good person. I never hurt anyone intentionally.
- I have helped others so much.
- This isn't fair.
- I was just about to retire.
- I still have kids.
- It wasn't my fault.
- I am educated.
- I am financially well off.
- I have too many important things to do.
- I already have too many problems.
- I already have one illness.

Illness is the great equalizer. No one is exempt. If you continue to think you are in some way privileged and should not be included as among those eligible for illness, you are more likely to be disgruntled, disappointed or despairing.

What's the good news?

You had three operations in four days. Kidney failure. Respiratory failure. A small heart attack. In intensive care for a week on a respirator. You have lots of pain. The prognosis is so-so. What on earth could be the good news?

The nurse is holding your hand.

Your wife is still visiting.

No one has asked you to sign a piece of paper that looks like a will.

Your Aunt Bertha isn't allowed in.

There are no mosquitoes in intensive care.

It is raining so you couldn't have done the yard work anyway.

People will excuse you from remembering birthdays.

Your doctor is not going on vacation this week.

When you recover, peeing on your own will be a highlight.

No one is asking you to volunteer to help with the bottle drive.

In many situations we don't normally even think of using the "lens of good news." We don't think of looking beyond the obvious dilemma, difficulties, discouragements or even ugliness of the situation. Yet, perhaps that is the very time when we need to ask ourselves, intentionally, "what's the good news?" What, in this situation, do you need to notice is present, or even absent, that will even momentarily draw you away from the obvious down sides of the situation?

Influence the policy makers

Ever wonder, "what does it take before the policy makers will help?" Ever think that if someone in power or someone they loved got the condition you have, things might move ahead more quickly? There is a general sense that people with influence don't care. Yet...

- Betty Ford has done wonders for bringing drug and alcohol problems out in the open.

- Elizabeth Taylor has raised a lot of money and awareness for AIDS.

- Christopher Reeves has turned the eyes of America toward spinal cord injuries.

- Perhaps one of the reasons the whole world loved and mourned the loss of Princess Di was that she had influence *and* she cared.

People in public life are courted for their sponsorship or affiliation with a cause. Why wait for them to influence those in public office? Write to your government representative. Support a group that lobbies for research funds and services to those with the condition you have. Keep the issues in front of them. And don't be humble!

- Send newspaper clippings.

- Tell your personal story.

- Send an e-mail.

- Join a group that will act collectively.

- Send photos!

Let go of the idea that life is fair and logical

If life was fair and people were logical, wealth wouldn't be concentrated in the bank accounts of just a few. Everyone would be loved. The legal system would make no mistakes. Our kids would appreciate us. More people would think like we do. Friends wouldn't disappear when you get ill. Whoever used the last sheet of toilet tissue would hang up the next roll. We would have no homeless children, and cars would not be allowed to travel at speeds greater than safety dictates. Accidents by stupidity would be non-existent.

But life is not fair and the world is not run according to logic.

Have you noticed?

Keep company with positive folks

It seems there is only one thing worse than being ill. That's being ill and alone. Some people, though, boost your hope more than others do. It's not surprising that research has confirmed our common sense understanding that patients are influenced by the people in their world, and vice versa.[24] Being ill is undoubtedly tough on the patient. The added demands of an ill family member or friend wear down loved ones. Attitudes are catchy.

Being negative on your part or theirs is best taken simply as a signal that there is something that needs dealing with which is presently being neglected. It is the *moping* that tells us that the hoping and coping are down a pint. Being negative can signal an unmet need, an unresolved feeling, an exhausted body, or an overextended self. Strange as this may seem, it's healthy. It is the red light on your emotional dashboard.

What's unhealthy is being around someone who is a perpetual cynic, who feels he has a right to blame you or others for his negative destiny—over and over. It's even harder if you are dependent upon them for your care.

Take a moment to ask yourself: who is influencing your perspective and in what direction? Whose attitude are you influencing? In what direction?

Eat dessert first

Illness is a time when you get to notice what is important, when you get to change how you do things, when you realize how fragile life is and how quickly it passes, and when you recognize whether or not you have been in a rut.

At a time when I had to rely on baby food, I took two jars to my niece's ball tournament. Arriving at the ball game for the top of the fifth, I opened the peaches and spooned them in while I watched the youngsters slug themselves out of a four-point hole. Two homers gave them an additional edge. The top of the second jar resisted my effort so I turned to my husky brother to rescue me. He stared at the putrid green matter asking with a curled lip and raised eyebrows, "Is that dessert?" I replied, "Certainly not, this is peas and carrots. I ate the peaches first. That's my new philosophy in life: 'eat dessert first.'"

Reflections on Attitude

- *What things do you tend to do to be the "good" patient?*

- *What could you say the next time you feel tempted to say, "I'm sorry"?*

- *Has something ever turned out better than you expected?*

- *What do you hope science will develop?*

- *With whom would you be willing to trade lousy situations?*

- *What would it be like to be in a war zone and have your condition?*

- *What were you taught about the role of suffering in life?*

- *How much would it help you to understand "why"?*

- *How do you explain why things go wrong?*

- *What immunity to illness did you think you had?*

- *What's one good thing that you notice in your situation? (Remember, it can be small.)*

- *What could you do to advocate for direct services or research?*

- *About what in your situation can you say, "This is unfair," or "this is illogical"? Can you accept that life can be unfair, and people can be illogical?*

- *Who could you be in touch with today who is positive?*

- *Have you been in a rut? What would be your version of "eating dessert first"?*

Your Body

Give your body a chance

The body never lies.
—Verena Kast[25]

When the red light on our car's dashboard comes on, we pull over into a service station, often not risking the long journey home. Yet, when the equivalent red lights go on in our bodies, we often drive on. Sure enough, the cold develops into pneumonia, the fatigue brings on a full-fledged reoccurrence of fibromyalgia, or an unattended cut becomes host to an infection.

We live in our bodies. There is no getting around it. Making friends with our bodies is important. Our bodies are not our enemies. Our body is doing the best it can. What it needs is a friend who respects its strengths and limitations.

Just as friendships have to be nourished, so do our bodies. They need to be nourished with rest, with food, with touch, with exercise and with humor. Friendships deepen with time and with increased knowledge of each other. As you come to know your body, listen to it. In turn, it will do its best to make your life enjoyable.

Respect your symptoms

Having just moved, my husband and I hadn't yet stocked up on groceries. The array of empty pizza boxes and an empty fridge meant we needed to go out to get something for lunch. It was only 11 o'clock. Surely I could make it until noon. We left at 11:30. As I entered the store I felt the telltale shakiness and my perspiration told me of a deepening problem. The first display table had a carton of fresh dates. They would do. Abandoning pursuit of anything with protein, I was grateful the cash register lane was open. Putting down $10.00 and starting to pry open the container, the clerk hesitantly offered me my change and asked, "Are you okay?" Inside I wanted to yell, "No, stupid. Can't you see I am about to faint?" Instead I apologetically blurted out, "Can you help me open this? I need to have some sugar." What ensued was quite funny. She broke two pens prying off the lid before I started stuffing myself with the food of the gods. Other than that, the shopping trip was perfectly normal.

How do you know when to ignore a symptom and when to respect it as a messenger of the body? All of us have had the experience of ignoring a headache because we were engrossed in an activity, only to realize upon completion that our headache had vanished. And we have all had the experience of ending up in more serious difficulties because we chose to ignore a warning sign.

Have you caught yourself noticing the symptoms and yet denying the need to do anything? It is always easier to look back and say:

- I knew that migraine was coming on.

- I was just exhausted, but I thought I could finish.

- I knew I was running a fever, but...

If you don't feel well, it is probably because you are not well. Symptoms are the body's language, the body's messengers. They are how your body tells you to pay attention to something. Killing the symptom is not always the answer. Many people learn to avoid episodes or relapses of their condition by recognizing the symptoms early, often earlier than they are observable to family or physicians. Yet it is not always easy to let yourself act on those signals without the permission or acknowledgment of others. It is up to you whether you will listen when your body whispers there is a problem coming, or whether later it will have to scream to get your attention.

Rest

There is a cure for most fatigue. It's called rest. It's nature's repair time. Pushing yourself extends the recovery time. Yes, it is important to push the boundaries, to see what you can do. But then you must rest. Extend, then rest. Sometimes just rest.

Resting doesn't necessarily mean sleep, although sleep is a remarkable state. Lack of sleep can lead to death faster than lack of food.[26] Resting and sleeping are amazingly complex activities. And here you thought you were doing nothing!

Many of us have learned to think of ourselves as lazy if we are doing nothing. What if you were able to think of your "work" as recovering or sustaining well being? Resting is then a task. On occasion, it may even be an unwelcome task.

Moms are supposed to be moms under all circumstances. It is hard to say "no" to baking the brownies or attending the soccer game. Can a child understand when mom says, "I have to rest"? Maybe not. Regardless, it is not always possible to wait to be ill until your children are grown up or for them to be in school in order for you to rest. If you are a mom with limited energy, what could you do to feel okay about resting? Dads need to answer the same question.

Without enough sleep, our judgment falters, our motivation diminishes, our problem-solving ability wanes and our moods change. We simply cannot function well without adequate sleep. But what's adequate? People vary as to how much sleep they need. While some may do fine on six hours, others need a generous nine. For some, naps are beneficial.[27] The first step is a decision to get the rest that you need.

❧ *Returning to work after a year of serious illness, Barb accepted that, for a time, trying to work a full day would likely drain her. She bought a good foldout lawn chair, and brought in a comfy sheep skin and a favorite afghan. Each day when others took their lunch break, Barb headed for a book closet and a 45-minute rest. Initially it was hard not to join the others, but soon it became a welcome routine with the expected benefit of replenishing her energy.*

❧ *Janet was home following surgery. Unfortunately, her husband had become seriously ill a short time after her release. The daily demands, simple as they were (dishes, clean up, a bit of laundry, a few groceries, answering the phone) proved to be taxing. Almost unnoticeably, she slipped back into unwellness until the need to rest surfaced as a non-negotiable. She listened to her body and learned to rest regularly. Only then, inch by inch, did her strength return.*

Hospitals are not great places to get rest. The average uninterrupted sleep in an intensive care unit is eight minutes. If you are lucky, you might get a 20 minute nap.[28] Learn more about sleep, sleep habits and sleep inhibitors. Read. Get on the Internet. Ask your doctor for help. Ask your pharmacist. The old saying, "You need your sleep," is true.

Can you say, "It's okay for me to rest"?

Eat well

❦ *I used to eat chips every day, not to mention chocolate bars... but that was part of the hopeless situation I felt myself in. I felt out of control so I just shoved whatever garbage I could find in my face.*

Some people go so far as to say, "you are what you eat." Whatever your views are on what you consume, it doesn't take a nutritionist to know that good food, freshly prepared is better for you than junk food. With the exception of the occasional comfort food, a decision to eat well is a decision to help yourself get well and stay well.

If you have never paid serious attention to what you eat except for what your palate prefers, consider taking advantage of a professional nutritionist to guide you. Many health services provide this service for free. Changing your eating habits is like changing any habit. It can take time. It can feel foreign. It can have enormous benefits.

Red meat? Vegetarian? Organic? Processed or no processed foods? Choices, choices, choices. On the average visit to a supermarket, we are faced with about 30,000 choices of what to put in our carts. When you're ill, it's especially important to make good choices. You wouldn't walk out in front of traffic or put your hand in a fire, so why would you eat what you know is unhealthy? Maybe, like many others, you eat to escape. However, not all overeating is a deep psychological problem. It can just be a habit. It tastes good.

The media make sure we see food on television many times during a one-hour program. Research has shown a positive relationship between the number of hours of television viewing and the likelihood of being overweight.[29,30] Television is also putting our children at risk for obesity. This may not be surprising when you consider that over 90 percent of advertised foods are high in fat, sugar and/or salt.[31]

Some folks eat to live, while others live to eat. Some don't think much about it. Some decide to take charge. They go on a diet. These days there is a diet to cure this and a diet to cure that. However, diets are notoriously not the answer. They may even contribute to weight gain over the long haul.[32, 33] Weight loss is more likely to be sustained if exercise is part of the weight loss program.[34]

If you have a condition that necessitates certain food limitations, things will be more challenging. Healthy eating takes on new meaning. For example, celiac patients who respect the need to stay gluten-free are less likely to develop bowel cancer. That would seem like a reasonable incentive.

Think about it. What do you crave that isn't healthy for you? Even as I write this, I want to go and get that marshmallow. I try to ask the deeper question. What am I really craving? Solace? A friend? A hug? Quiet time? Laughter? Would I really feel any better having that junk food?

What is one small dietary change you could start today?

Know your comfort foods

It is all well and good to be disciplined about what goes into our bodies, but there are times in life when rigidity should be cast aside. Comfort foods can do something that a back rub, medication or a good conversation cannot. Yet if you overdose on them, they are no longer comfort foods, they are ordinary indulgences. You have to learn when comfort food has crossed over into another category.

Comfort food has to be savored. It is eaten as if it is sacrificed to the Gods of Well-Being. If it is homemade, it is prepared with love. If it is purchased at a special outlet, it helps if the waiter knows you by name and you can linger at a table while you eat it. It needn't be expensive and is rarely complicated. You may or may not know how it became a source of comfort for you. But you know it is.

Popcorn.

Chocolate ice-cream.

Chicken soup.

Teriyaki back ribs roasted until the meat falls off the bone.

Mangoes pureed and made into popsicles.

Comfort food does not have to make sense.

Use those dollars wisely

Illness and disability are costly. Even if you have adequate medical and disability coverage or live in a country with socialized medicine, there are additional costs. Most states in the U.S. have some form of health care available for everyone. Those who are privately insured may have greater access. If you feel health care needs to be more universally and equally available, many lobbying organizations would appreciate your help.

Giving your body a chance means being willing to spend part of your income on taking care of it. That could mean spending money on the basics of health care, or on some of the more pleasant indulgences. If money is no concern, you might want to ask yourself what you could do to more enjoy the money you have. You would be surprised how sharing some of it satisfies the soul.

If you have to watch your pennies, what could you do during this time to be a good steward of your money?

- Stay away from big-ticket items.
- Instead of a cruise ship, consider a canoe trip.
- Instead of dining out, go on a picnic.

Talk to someone you trust. If your debts are accumulating, a credit counselor can be helpful. Some financial and government institutions provide these services free of charge. That makes sense. You already owe too many people. If the issue is managing your existing resources, a financial planner can advise you. Keep in mind, though, that many of them are also salespeople for particular financial strategies.

Whether you have a large or a small income, think about keeping track of where you spend your dollars. You might be surprised.

> ❦ *One morning, a guest in our home made a comment to me as she watched me juice a fresh grapefruit. Her words, "It must be expensive to eat like you do," had a cutting edge to them. After deciding not to flash a dirty look at her for assuming anything about my money management, I explained that, even if it was expensive to eat healthy, illness would cost more. When I went on to explain that grapefruits this week were 5 for 79 cents and that my freshly-squeezed juice was worth 16 cents of my hard-earned money, a discussion about how to get the greatest nutritional value for our dollar ensued. (I still wanted to tell her it was none of her business, but this was far more constructive.)*

Stay in touch

Skin is the human body's largest organ. It accounts for 18 percent of our body weight and covers about 19 square feet.[35] We should take at least as good a care of it as we do of our carpets! If we don't care for it, we will become ill.

Premature infants studied at the Touch Research Institute demonstrate the importance of touch. Given three massages a day for ten days, a premature child can be expected to be more alert, active and responsive than infants of equal size and condition who do not receive a massage. The infant who is touched is better able to tolerate noise and to calm himself. He will sleep more deeply. He will have fewer episodes of apnea (a brief cessation of breathing).[36] He will gain weight 47 percent faster and be out of hospital an average of six days sooner.

In what would now be considered an absurd experiment to find out what language infants would naturally learn to speak, German emperor Frederick II seized a number of newborns from their parents in the year 1248. The nurses were instructed to feed but were not to cuddle nor talk to the infants. All died before they could talk, proving at that time that, "they could not live without petting." As recently as the 1990s, thousands of infants who were warehoused in orphanages in Romania and deprived of attention were found to have serious delays in their development.

Touch is a primal need. It is the first sense to develop and likely the last to fade. There are as many as 3,000 touch receptors in a fingertip and perhaps as many as five million in our skin. The benefits of touch are well established and extensive, and include lowering blood pressure, easing breathing, relieving stress, strengthening the immune system and enhancing sleep.[37]

We are touchy about touch. In many social situations, touch is considered taboo. You have to decide based on your own comfort level who can touch you, when, and in what way.

- It is okay to ask someone you trust to give you a back rub or to rub your feet.

- It is okay to touch yourself.

- Hug someone or something.

Don't be surprised if a few tears come along with the touching. Sometimes when we are ill, we get "out of touch" with our feelings. It happens inadvertently as we struggle with the day-to-day, trying to ignore or deny symptoms so we can function. In the process, we end up getting out of touch with our feelings. It happens. Our physical and emotional selves are connected.

Hug a Molly

Molly is our dog. She has one blue eye, one brown eye. She is half Siberian Husky and half Rhodesian Ridgeback, which means she has a hound's face that half pleads, half projects total disinterest in the world. At one point I was a pretty weak puppy myself. I had lost more than thirty pounds prior to surgery while they figured out what the problem was. By the time the decision to resect my blocked intestine came, I was weak and malnourished. The convalescence had not gone smoothly. The gut simply didn't want to wake up and start moving again. Eventually things were corrected, and I went home to recover.

Molly had been staying with my nephew during my illness. Allen, my husband, brought her back home after I had a day or two to adjust to being home myself. When they arrived I was sitting in a wheelchair in our large entryway. Coming through the back door, Molly saw me, bounded toward me—and then just stopped. She paused for a moment, walked slowly towards me, looked up and laid her head upon my lap. She knew. She just knew. And I loved her for it.

Molly loves to go for walks. She is young enough to still bound after butterflies and obedient enough not to make me run after her. If I get too far behind, she runs back and checks on me. Then she forges ahead toward whatever adventures might be under the next clump of bushes.

When I am not well enough to walk her, she appears grateful to sit on the top step of the porch with her two front paws on the next lower step, and respectfully be doted upon. Often she simply puts her head against mine,

I tell her the woes of the day and we both seem to know. Know what? I'm not sure. It just seems like we both understand something. And she offers no unsolicited advice.

If you don't have a Molly, the neighbors will probably be willing to loan their dog on occasion. Or, when someone is coming to visit, ask if they would bring their well-behaved Malamute. Yes, there will be a few dog hairs, but there will also be a wagging tail to go with them.

Some institutions have pet visitation programs. A veterinarian has checked all of the visiting animals. Someone who normally visits in the local seniors home with their pet might be willing to visit your home as well.

Or, if you are well enough and you have an obedient dog, think about taking your Molly and brightening someone else's day.[38,39]

Exercise

Exercise? Am I crazy? Maybe, but I don't think so. I am not talking about training for the marathon. I am talking about the known relationship between physical and mental well being. There is also the issue of muscle tone.

You don't need to join a gym. Your house likely has potential for a little circuit training. Little knee bends holding onto the banister. Leg lifts, little ones, holding onto the kitchen counter. A few stretches in the front of the bay window. Up and down the stairs once a day as soon as you are strong and stable enough. Two soup cans, one in each hand, doing a few wrist curls while you watch your favorite television show. It's a start.

Don't forget there are also opportunities to get some physical exercise during everyday, household activities. Use a hand-held can opener rather than an electric one. Put the sauce pans on a lower shelf or drawer and when you need one use the opportunity to do a knee bend. Do five pelvic tilts before you get out of bed in the morning. Use your towel vigorously after a shower, and sing along with the motion.

When you are stronger, there is the garden. Just try a little at a time. You can graduate to walking the dog. If you don't have a dog, borrow one. The neighbor would probably willingly release Fido for an extra walk. Perhaps you could borrow a terrier first. You can work your way up to the Great Dane.

When you are ready, try a yoga or Feldenkrais exercise class. Graduate from something gentle before joining a karate class. In *Growing Old Is Not for Sissies,*[40] you will find a photograph of a 90-year-old woman who is about to try for her black belt in karate. If she can do it, who knows what you can do?

If you have osteoporosis, it might be best to abandon thoughts of playing football with the kids next door. It is advised that you consult a physician or physical therapist about what is within your bounds. But remember, it is your body. You will know how much it can do at any given time. Listen to it. Its wonderful gift to you is that even your bones will strengthen if you exercise.

Once you start a walking program, you may even notice side benefits, like my friend did:

❦ *I realize one of the reasons my walks are so pleasant is that I now have several people I see everyday and say "Hello!" to. I also smile and say "hello" to anyone who makes eye contact, and sometimes even if they don't.*

Do some "inner jogging"

How long since you experienced a "physiological reflex; a successive, rhythmic, spasmodic expiration with open glottis and vibration of the vocal cords, often accompanied by a baring of teeth and facial grimaces"? In other words: a good, hearty laugh? Laughter has been called "inner jogging."[41] It has actual physiological benefits. Norman Cousins claimed that during a period of time when he was fighting a life-threatening illness, ten minutes of belly laughter would give him two hours of pain-free sleep.

Four-year-olds laugh once every four minutes. Over the years we are told to wipe that smile off of our faces, for "life is serious." Illness in particular is no laughing matter. Yet under what circumstances do more absurd things happen? You are supposed to be able to pee in a bottle, rest in the middle of a high tech trauma unit, keep 300 pills a day straight, be cordial while you swallow barium, feel confident when you are in a silly-looking gown, be happy to see relatives who never visited you when you were well, let people wash you where normally only you wash you, and not worry when your young, competent replacement at work visits and tells you everything is under control and she loves the work... it was exactly what she was trained for.

Now you need your sense of humor more than ever! It helps if your physician has one, too. The first time we visited my husband Allen's physician, we were taken by the fact that rather than pictures of the city skyline, reprints of Renoir, or cutesy posters that are cheaper by the dozen, his walls were plastered with medical humor. Here was a man who could laugh at himself and at the situations in which he found himself. Over the years, and without either doctor or patient bashing, he has helped us through many a difficult time.

Can you work at humor? It shouldn't be work. It is a mindset. Just start to notice funny, unusual and bizarre things in every day life.

* *Jack, a patient of mine, and his friend Boris were out golfing one day. Both had advanced cancer. Boris was complaining about the condition of the course. "These greens look terrible."*

  Jack retorted, "They look better from this side." A moment of puzzlement was followed by a hearty laugh from Boris who suddenly realized exactly what Jack meant.

Readers Digest's "Laughter Is the Best Medicine" is a good place to start. Cartoons are great, too. Ask people to bring you one. Try to have one joke to tell each person who visits. Ask yourself, "What in this situation could possibly be funny when I am telling about it sometime in the future?"

Record the funny moments

In the Meaningful Life Therapy cancer treatment program at the Shibata Hospital in Kurashiki, Japan, patients are asked to report what was funny about being a cancer patient that week. Think about it. There is undoubtedly something funny about your situation if you can step back from it for a moment. During the next week, watch for at least three things, that, if you looked at them differently, you could see some humor in. Write them down here, and you can claim that you helped write this book.

Mufty has started your list with:

1. Take a camera to the hospital and photograph the x-ray techs photographing you. It's really fun.

2.

3.

4.

Grow something

If you have a garden and a library, you have everything you need.
—Tullius Cicero

If I get down, I go to the garden and I hoe like mad.
—Dawn Jevne

Grow something:

Inside.

Outside.

Large.

Small.

Just grow something!

❧ *Still confined to the house, Lora was delighted to receive a miniature herb garden in a container. All summer, the chives, peppers, celery, parsley and herbal surprises garnished her salads. It wasn't long before she was reading books on herbs as well as benefiting from the produce. The initial, "Oh, no! I don't know anything about gardening," was soon forgotten with the joy of watching her little garden produce.*

Get those hands into the soil. Let yourself smell the fragrances. Watch something grow. Feel the wind and sun. Gardening is fast becoming the nation's most popular hobby. Many an amateur gardener will attest to the benefits of having your fingers in the "healing fields."[42]

Talk to your body

When you talk to your body, you are simply acknowledging it and encouraging it. You assure it that you are a willing friend and will do the best for both of you. Some things you might say would be:

I care about you.

It is hard, but we can make progress.

We can do this!

Maybe not right now, but we will.

Take little steps.

Time to dust ourselves off again!

I will try to make good choices for both of us.

What else does your body want to hear?

1.

2.

Now go back and say them out loud. Louder. Louder yet! Have someone join you. First thing you know, you will be laughing or crying.

Either way, you will know you are alive.

Have a soothsayer

A soothsayer is a prognosticator, someone who predicts how things are going to turn out. Each of us can benefit from someone who says with conviction: "It's going to be okay." That doesn't mean things necessarily will turn out the way we would prefer, but it does mean that we will be okay no matter how they turn out. They can also say other things that help us feel that things really will be okay in some way. For instance:

Hang in there.

Yes, you can!

I will be here for you.

No matter what happens, the strength will come.

Forget perfection.

Go, Kid, go!

Worry about your mother later.

There are always surprises in life.

Who might be willing to be your soothsayer? Explain the role and see who's interested.

Get a wellness coach

When you train for a marathon, you may have a coach. Getting well can feel like a marathon, so why not have a wellness coach?

What does a coach do? A couch encourages you. He (or she) has expectations that you will continue your training program. He confronts you if you appear not to be committed. He helps you define and focus on your goals. He keeps you from sabotaging yourself by creating unrealistic goals. He is there for you if you have an injury or a setback. Yet, a coach does not take responsibility for you. You can confide in a coach, and yet you don't have to be close friends with him. A coach is not there at your beck and call, but he is there for your triumphs and tragedies. This is someone you can trust.

Talk to such a person about the role you would like them to play in your life. They will need to think it over.

> ❦ *I knew somewhat by accident who was to be my coach. I was back in hospital with an attack after months of feeling well. Things weren't looking that great, and I knew I would require considerable discipline to get out of the hole again. Instinctively I called Trudy and asked if she would come to the hospital. She knows me well and she knew that as soon as I was holding food again, I would be back at my workaholic pattern. I love my work, but my body gets overextended. I needed someone to remind me in no*

uncertain terms that I had new limits. She agreed, and did.
And I got well.

You can have more than one wellness coach. Different people can help us with different aspects of our recovery or adjustment. A coach is someone who pushes you to do your best. He or she is not just a friend who provides encouragement when you are down. They have a specific assigned role.

Be cautious about self-appointed coaches. They are people who come out with, "This is how we are going to do it," even before you have asked them for help. They may be intent only on your achieving their version of wellness.

In addition, it might be good to have a wellness buddy. This is more of a companion than a coach. They, too, may be getting well, or they may have been through something similar. A wellness buddy befriends you. They may say, "Yeah, you can do what the coach is asking. Hang in there! It will be okay." Then they add, "Wanna' go for an ice cream?"

Learn to "park it"

Some days are just too much. There is too much going on physically, emotionally—you name it. It might be the day you get word you did not get the part-time job that would put you back in the job market. Or it might be the day your son gets sent home from school for fighting on the playground. Or, maybe your grandchild broke an ornament that was your first anniversary gift. It could be that you are worrying that this whole situation is taking too much of a toll on your spouse.

You do need to deal with these things—in the near future. Today, just park it. I used to call this strategy, "put it on the shelf." I would lie down or sit in the big chair in the living room and envision placing all of my worries on an imaginary shelf, knowing I could take them down one at a time. One day, during a particularly difficult time, I was consciously putting things on the shelf when my imagination startled me. The shelf broke! As a result, now I use a parking lot. On a parking lot I can drive the thoughts and worries to new locations. If necessary, the parking lot can be expanded.

It's okay to park things for a short period of time. How do you do it? Put you brain in neutral. Take your mind off the gas. Turn off the motor. Do a jigsaw puzzle. Watch a mindless movie. Knit. Bake. Work in your shop. Gardening works well, too. Go window-shopping. Play solitaire or a good game of cribbage. Surf on the Internet. If the worrisome thoughts slip back in, put on the emergency brake and say, "Stay parked! I am not dealing with you right now." Write it out in a journal. Put it on an index card. Slip it into your Bible. Put it in the job jar.

You can ask others to "park it," too. Not all problems have to be discussed when they first come up. Sometimes you need time to let your whole self find a rightful place for whatever is going on. After doing well for years, a recurrence of illness is going to start a thousand thoughts. You don't have to decide anything until you have had a little time. For those folks who are nattering about what you should do, explain you would appreciate them "parking it" for a few days.

Take the pressure off.
Simply don't demand anything of your body or mind.

Reflections on Your Body

♥ *Which symptom do you most commonly ignore?*

♥ *What message is your body attempting to send to you?*

♥ *What would have to happen for you to get additional rest?*

♥ *What is one unhealthy thing you could take out of your fridge or cupboards?*

♥ *What is one healthy food your could put in your fridge or cupboards?*

♥ *What are your three favorite comfort foods?*

♥ *What is your favorite casserole? Who makes it best?*

♥ *If you had only $7.00 with which to enjoy yourself, what would you do?*

♥ *Have you had your hug today?*

♥ *What exercise could you do today?*

♥ *What amused you today?*

♥ *Animal, mineral or vegetable? What new living thing could you introduce into your life?*

♥ *What would you like to say to your body? What does your body want to say to you?*

♥ *What is the one phrase that seems to help more than any other?*

♥ *Who could be your wellness coach? Your wellness buddies?*

♥ *Is there anything you would like to "park" for a few days?*

♥ *Where are you going to park it?*

The Health Care System

Give health care a chance

When you get right down to it, it's really a partnership.
We depend on them and they depend on us.[43]

It's not all up to you. Yet neither is it all up to the health care professionals. It is unfair to ask them to do the impossible. No amount of information, intervention or caring will make a difference if you are not open to helping yourself. Hoping means being open to a future in which you are willing to participate.

What can you do? You can cooperate by becoming well informed, dealing with the realities of your condition, and reaching out for help when you need it. Taking advantage of the resources available to you can lead to possibilities you otherwise might not have discovered. Making effective use of the health care system doesn't mean you can't also benefit from less scientific alternatives. It is crucial you are able to sort out what is useful to you.

Be aware, however, that charlatans do exist. They lie in wait for vulnerable people to grasp at straws while writing out their checks. To be a well-informed partner in your health management, use all the resources you can to become as well as you can.

Become knowledgeable

Ignorance rarely helps in difficult circumstances. If you have your head in the sand, it keeps you from looking for alternatives. Granted, it may also help you to temporarily deny what you are afraid of. Today's health care consumer needs to be at least somewhat informed. But how much knowledge, and from what sources? Many people spend more time planning a vacation or looking at house plans than they do learning about their bodies or conditions.

You want to turn to trustworthy information sources. Three sources of information we expect to be credible are physicians, published reading materials and self-help groups. Yet, it is still important to recognize the strengths and limitations of each.

Obviously talking to your physician is a good place to start. Remember, though, that not all physicians are able to focus on the positive. A friend recently received two different viewpoints with the same diagnosis and the same set of laboratory results. One reliable source suggested that only 20 percent of people survive her condition. A second opinion from a very reputable research center suggested the odds were closer to 50 percent. Even credible sources may differ in their interpretations of information.

Another tactic is reading. Read about the condition. Read about how to manage the condition. Bibliotherapy, as it is called, is known to influence our attitudes and to assist in changing our behavior.[44-46] Like many strategies we can use, reading is not without its risks. We can get misinformation from minimally researched materials. We can get

70

information that is persuasive because its intent is to sell you something. We can also get very credible information but misinterpret it. We can get mixed messages from different people writing from experience in different settings. Sometimes there just is not enough known to get consistent information, and we have to accept that the best information available is still only opinion based on limited understanding and good intentions. If you are fortunate, your hospital or community health center has a resource center with trained personnel to assist in recommending sources, acquiring and interpreting information.

Often, major self-help organizations have established bibliographies. They can recommend to you books, pamphlets and Internet sites that are trustworthy. Yes, it takes time.

Becoming knowledgeable doesn't only mean reading. It means discussing and experimenting, sorting the chaff from the wheat. It means asking questions, and then asking more questions.

Make use of the Internet

The wonderful thing about the Internet is that somewhere along the line you are going to get distracted. You can start out to see what the herbal remedies for nausea are, and you end up in a website about herbal gardens, which takes you to a website about gardens in general, which takes you to a site about bird baths, that leads you to a site about snowy owls... because you think you saw one last winter and it was so beautiful.

What's your excuse for not using the Internet? Are you technophobic? When something goes wrong, are you convinced that the computer is trying specifically and personally to frustrate you? Or maybe you can't type? Or you're afraid you will end up in cyberspace and no one will find you? Despite your fears, the Internet is actually remarkably friendly and even people who are ill and who do not have a lot of energy can use it. If you need to, get a half-hour of instruction from a patient person to get started.

If you don't have a computer yourself, don't worry. Undoubtedly someone you know is connected to the Web, or you can go to your local library. A librarian can help get you started.

There are web pages for almost every health condition. Sure, you will have to sort out what is most useful for you. The online discussion groups can be encouraging and supportive, too. You can ask questions, seek information or give your opinion. Your physician might even allow you to use their information to gain access to medical literature sites.

Choose what you read carefully

Do you want to feel better? Then read the books that appeal to you. And read only the sections that appeal to you. Reading can be a downer. If reading something makes you feel less adequate, less hopeful or less energetic, stop reading, or change books immediately. Even switch to reading a mystery. If you find out your situation is very, very serious, then stop reading about the condition. Instead, start reading about exceptions; about people who defied the odds.[47] There are also many books available that will show you how to overcome or manage an illness or difficult circumstances.

Testimonials and research substantiate that these approaches are often effective. However, *you* must decide what you are willing to try. Try one at a time. And give yourself breaks from always learning more... learning more... and learning more. There is no point in exhausting yourself as you try to get well.

If you can't afford to buy the books yourself, don't worry, people will inevitably loan you the book, the audiotape or the videotape that has helped them. Remember, though, if you're not enjoying it, put it down. It may make sense later. Or, it may not. In that case, don't worry, just skip it. You are not a failure if someone else's magic is not yours.

Find a patient-oriented physician

A good doctor-patient relationship is an important piece in the jigsaw puzzle of becoming and staying as well as possible.

Most of us want a doctor who treats us like a person, not like a disease. When we are ill, the patient-doctor relationship is the most important relationship we will have on some days. Way back in 1801, a medical school text suggested to would-be physicians that the key to "giving patients hope" was to gain their confidence.[48] The doctor-patient relationship is one of trust. In essence, it depends on "the patient's confidence that the physician will do what is best for the patient."[49]

One individual with AIDS described the importance of having a good patient-doctor relationship as the following:

> *When you have somebody who encourages you and makes you feel better, it gives that little edge... It gives you that important feeling inside... You have to have that special feeling with your physician...'cause that's when you get hope.*[50]

You and your doctor are a team. Team players have equal but different roles. Each maintains some control and some responsibility. When you have an office discussion with your doctor, does he interrupt it to answer the phone? Or does she leave the room? Is your doctor walking halfway down the hall before you know your appointment is over? Or does your doctor listen to you? Some physicians have the ability to help you feel that you are important to them. Some physicians communicate very well. Others do not.

The same could be said of patients. Physicians are not mind readers. You have to tell them your symptoms, your needs, and your preferences. Physicians differ on how open they are to "patients as partners." If a physician diminishes your hope, he or she is not a helpful team member, even if they claim to be doing so on behalf of making you realistic. Compassion without truth is unhelpful. Equally unhelpful is truth without compassion. Even if the eyes of medicine consider your condition to be hopeless, you as a person are not without hope.

How can you leave the doctor's office feeling confident? As a first step, take two index cards with you to the doctor's office. On one card, list all of the questions you have, and all of your symptoms. On the other card, write down the following checklist and refer to it before you leave.[51]

Diagnosis:

- Do I understand the diagnosis, what is causing my symptoms, how long they will last and the likely outcome of having them?

- Do I understand the treatment and the instructions?

Follow up:

- Do I know how I will be followed up? Should I return for a visit? If so, when? Should I phone for test results? Is there anything I should watch for and report back?

Action:

- What actions am I supposed to take? Repeat what you understand you are to do. If you don't understand, ask again.

Comply with treatment

I have a hip that gives me trouble on occasion. It gets inflamed. The answer is to stay off of it temporarily. A set of crutches occupies a space behind the front entry door. I only need them every couple of years. I know what to do to recover. I even know what to do to prevent the condition. But I still screw up. The last time I did it I was doing four public lectures in 24 hours in a small city. I traveled light. Despite knowing that high heels exacerbate the problem, I thought, "Oh, well," and somehow allowed myself to violate everything I know about how to stay out of hip pain. I ended up seeing the doctor, who ordered me to stay off of my hip and placed me on anti-inflammatory medication.

The rest of the story is simple. I wasn't compliant on either level of treatment, and as a result I put myself through additional weeks of agony. I am grateful, though, for the physician. She asked how consistently I had been off my feet. To my honest answer, she smiled and replied, "Well, I guess you prefer pain to comfort. Was there something else you were hoping I could do?" I smiled back and promised a more committed effort. A week later I was pain-free.

It is estimated that as many as 50 percent of people are not compliant with their medications.[52] That is, they either don't fill the prescription, they fail to take it regularly, or they don't complete the regime. As for other treatments—well, how faithfully do you follow medically-prescribed advice?

We have choices. We can decide with which treatments to comply. There may be reasons for rejecting some suggestions or interventions, but once we agree to comply, it isn't really fair to expect results without following through.

Somehow we want or expect to escape logical consequences. It rarely works.

Give up the search for the "magic bullet"

Books in the self-help health section of a bookstore emanate the message, "Buy me! I contain the magic bullet!" If you say the right prayers, wear the right crystals, surround yourself with the right colors, see the right doctors, repeat the magical affirmations, then you will be fine.

There are magic bullets for some things. However, for most, there are not. Even broken legs need time and rehabilitation. Chronic conditions are more like a jigsaw puzzle. You have to fit things in, piece by piece. If you are searching solely for the magic bullet, you will miss things that could help with 5 percent or 10 percent of the problem.

> ❦ *I would still like to find a magic bullet. Absolutely. The question, though, is what do I do while I am waiting for or searching for one? It's key to keep asking if one has been discovered. It's also key that I not just sit around waiting for a complete cure, while partial relief is available and within my reach.*

What is your version of the magic bullet? Are you hoping for surgery? A new medication? A vaccination? Good, keep hoping—even canvass for research money and petition government health policy makers. But in the meantime, check to see if you are bemoaning that a magic bullet isn't there. And check to see if there are little miracles right in front of you that you have missed. Deciding what to search for is not an easy choice, nor is it without its consequences.

❦ *Natalie was diagnosed with cancer of the uterus at 33 and immediately had a hysterectomy. Four years later, the cancer reappeared in several internal organs and in her bones. She and her husband, Phil, desperately searched for a doctor somewhere who would have the magic cure. They sought out magnetic treatments in Greece. Psychic surgery in Manila. Ancient herbs in Mexico... Eight months later, Natalie and Phil returned to Detroit. She now weighed 82 pounds. Their considerable savings were depleted. Entering a hospice, Natalie finally found relief from pain. Only days before her death, she shared with a caregiver: "I wonder what I've been looking for. I lost precious months when I could have been close to my family and friends, and for what?"*

Risk being misinterpreted

Do you do better with a hard chair than a soft one, but the only hard chair in the room is already taken? Do you have special diet restrictions but you don't want to scrape the gravy off the gourmet chicken your hostess has slaved over all afternoon? Would receiving pre-boarding assistance conserve your energy, but you have an invisible condition like heart disease and you don't want people to think you are an opportunist? Are you really too tired to go to that anniversary party, but you don't want to hurt anyone's feelings? Did you forget your medication, but don't want to bother anyone by asking them to drive you home to get it? Have you been programmed to be polite?

It is difficult to take care of ourselves in a world in which we have been programmed to be polite. There is a certain additional sanity to a world with social graces. However, when social acceptability interferes with health, something isn't right. Many of us need to practice giving ourselves permission to do what we need to do in the interests of our health, without worrying about being polite.

Say to yourself, "It's okay to do whatever I need to do to be as well and comfortable as possible." You might want to expand your list of permissions. Do you give yourself permission to:

Ask for what you need?

Say "no" when you feel "no"?

Say "yes" when you feel "yes"?

Eat what you need?

Travel where you want?

Bring along what you need?

If you could grant yourself permission to do three things that would add to your comfort or health, what would they be?

1.

2.

3.

Ask for a referral

If for any reason you doubt the diagnosis, the prognosis, or the treatment recommendations suggested by your doctor, you may feel ill-equipped to make the necessary decisions. As well, if you are told there is nothing that can be done to improve your situation, then it is only natural that you might want to get a second opinion. If you have three choices about what to do, you might want the views of more than one experienced person. It is *your* life. You have a right to the most accurate information available to you. Specialists will vary in their knowledge and in their opinions about what constitutes "fact" in any given situation.

You may be hesitant to ask for a second opinion, fearful that it may affect the doctor-patient relationship on which you are now dependent. But a confident physician has no reason to resent your wanting to confirm the degree of difficulty you might be facing. A compassionate physician would not deny you the opportunity to explore every possibility. If you need a second—or even a third—opinion to gather more information or to come to terms with the first information, you usually need to ask for the referral.

That's right:

Just ask.

It doesn't hurt to just happen to have the name of one or two other doctors who are considered excellent! And it doesn't hurt to have someone with you who expresses the need on behalf of the whole family.

Ask for a second opinion

That's right:

Just ask.

If your physician is so sure of the diagnosis and prognosis, it shouldn't be a problem to have it confirmed. Yes, it could potentially offend your physician. Yes, sometimes they can be annoyed, even irked. Other physicians, however, are pleased to share the responsibility with another colleague. Do your best to request politely and to describe how having a second opinion might help you deal with the situation better.

A second opinion is not always soothing. If it confirms the first catastrophic opinion, it may be unsettling. If the opinion is different from the first opinion, that, too, may be confusing.

Medicine is simply not a clear-cut science. Often a second opinion that is in agreement with the first can help us to come to terms with the condition. We must adjust and plan. Or, if the second opinion is in disagreement with the first, we are allowed more hope and we may derive energy from the thought of possibility. Either can be important.

Realize there are more treatments than your doctor prescribes

The limits of medicine are not the limits of the body's potential to recover or the mind's ability to adjust. There is a litany of other possibilities, some of which will be more helpful than others depending on the condition. Some treatments are considered well within traditional approaches. Others are considered complementary or even unconventional. It is estimated that in 1990, Americans made 425 million visits to providers of alternative therapies.[53] Examples of such therapies include:

- Physical therapy
- Occupational therapy
- Herbs
- Massage
- Reiki
- Acupuncture
- Naturopathy
- Prayer
- Humor
- Art therapy
- Drama therapy
- Aromatherapy
- Pet therapy
- Horticulture therapy
- Music therapy

- Talk-to-an-old-friend therapy
- Keeping a journal
- Tai chi
- Phototherapy
- Biofeedback

If you don't know what some of these are, use your library card, search the Internet, or to talk to other patients who got well against the odds. Numerous organizations have also produced written guidelines that can help you assess the appropriateness of various treatment approaches for your condition.[54]

Are you worried that your doctor might not approve of unconventional or complementary therapies? Only 3 out of 10 people ever inform their doctors that they are using alternative therapies. The problem with telling them is that they may spit in your soup! In other words, they may discourage you. On the other hand, you are denying one of your most important health care partners the opportunity to support you in your efforts, to expand their understanding of what is helpful, and to be informed about what you are doing in case it affects future care.

Do you think of yourself as someone who doesn't try new things? Do you consider yourself "traditional" or "conventional"? Are you holding onto the idea that medicine alone is going to have the answer, and that doctors are responsible for your health? What would have to happen for you to consider additional possibilities?

Expect setbacks

Setbacks are difficult but common. Somehow when we start to feel better we think wellness should come in a tidy sequential series of progressions, the culmination of which is complete physical, mental, emotional and spiritual health. Most of the self-help books help us believe in the myth of total wellness. Larry Dossey reminds us:

> *Our bodies can act up, break down and get sick without ever consulting us. Failure to recognize the relative intractability of the flesh is one of the excesses of today's consciousness-and-health movement, and is the potential cause of immense guilt when things go wrong.*[55]

As much as each of us would like to be the exception, most of us are not. We live with chronic conditions and endure periodic flare-ups and setbacks. Search as we may, sometimes the flare-ups seem to come out of nowhere. Perhaps they do. Perhaps they don't. It almost feels better when we can say, "It was because of this or that," but the truth is, we can't always know how or why a setback arises. Sometimes reoccurrence appears to have a mind of its own. There is a good deal of mystery to life. Remember, you have not "failed" if a condition reappears.

Know your rights

At one time, we lived in an era of the family doctor and friend; however, now health care is based predominantly in scientific decision-making. The professional is the expert, and he or she makes all of the important decisions, and allocates the resources. In response to this silencing of patients' voices in deciding their own destiny, the concept of *patient rights* has emerged.

Patient rights outline what we have a right to expect from our health care providers and institutions. This can differ based on where we live, the condition from which we suffer, local legislation, and the policies of the insurance companies and other institutions that serve us.

Hopefully, you feel cared for and respected by those who provide your health care. If or when a difficult situation arises, however, it can be useful to know your rights. Most people don't think about rights until they suspect that theirs have been violated. Usually hospitals and care facilities have a formal list of "Patient Rights" available for your asking. Some hospitals even have patient advocates to assist you.

Typically, you have the right to be treated with compassion and respect; the right to a level of privacy; and the right to be informed about your condition and treatment. Facilities differ about the right to access your records and numerous other rights.

Why not be well informed?

Remember, with rights come responsibilities.
Check out what is expected of you.

Organize your health-related information

How many times do you have to tell your story? To the nurse. To the intern. To the doctor. To the doctor the first doctor referred you to. To the insurance company... What drugs are you on? When did you start taking them? Were you ever on Superpill 2000? When did you see Dr. So & So? Was that before or after you had your sixth operation? And on and on it goes.

Why not have a way to keep track of your health-related information? A simple binder will do. Have a section for appointments. Who did you see? What was the date? What was the outcome? The section on drugs needs to list your prescriptions and over-the-counter medications. When did you have the prescription filled? What was it for? How much did you take? Often pharmacists provide information about those "wonder" drugs in case you ever wonder what they do. Include any drug information handouts in your binder. Information you found on the Internet may also be filed alphabetically by topic.

It is also useful to have a section that allows you to notice your progress and your setbacks. By taking stock of your strengths, resources, concerns and options during one period of time, you provide yourself with a baseline or yardstick to refer to over time. A section for your correspondence and one for a few personal notes will top it off. Your efforts at being organized don't have to be sophisticated to work.

If you are serious about assessing your situation and organizing your health-related information, write to Hope House and we will, for a small fee, send you a copy of *Hope, Health and Taking Charge*.[56] The publication is designed to guide you through the process of assessing your situation and organizing your information. You write right in it. It is small enough to be unobtrusive, and simple enough not to be overwhelming.

People who alphabetize their spices and hang their clothes from light to dark easily adapt to record keeping. People who claim they work best under pressure and in chaos will not even consider it. Most of us fall somewhere in between. We could provide more accurate information more quickly with just a bit more thought.

Physicians may have mixed reactions when you come prepared with information and specific questions. Some physicians will welcome an organized, well-informed patient. Others may appear skeptical. Most do not appreciate people who waste their time—so, no novels! However, you also have the right to the effective use of your time. Some physicians will welcome a synopsis of your condition and treatment history. Others may seem reluctant to read such a summary. Regardless, ask that the synopsis you have written be placed in your medical record. Then answer the many questions which, had they read your summary, would already have been answered. Whether physicians ask you many questions or just a few, your task is to assist them by providing the information they need in order to help you.

Reflections on the Health Care System

- *How much do you really want to know about your condition?*

- *Who could help you to learn how to navigate the Internet?*

- *How close are you to overdosing on information?*

- *What have you read that has been helpful? Unhelpful?*

- *What is one small thing you could say or do that would improve your relationship with your physician?*

- *What part of treatment do you find difficult to comply with?*

- *How long do you plan to wait for the "magic bullet"?*

- *What do you do for "social" acceptance that you would like to stop doing?*

- *Is there a referral you would like to be able to discuss with your physician?*

- *What alternative treatment would you like to explore?*

- *What would constitute a setback for you? How do you plan to handle it?*

- *Which patient rights are you aware of?*

- *What color would you like the binder containing your medical information to be?*

Support

Coming to terms with who can help

I don't know how I would have made it without Irene.
She was there for me. She seemed to know what I needed.

I can't believe Bill could call himself a friend. I didn't
see him the whole time I was in intensive care.

Is Irene the "true friend," while Bill is the"fair-weather friend"? Perhaps not. What we do know is that Irene and Bill are different in how they relate to a person in times of crisis. Everyone has different strengths. We can have —in fact we *need* —a variety of friends with a variety of abilities, each one of whom gives us valuable support, differently.

The only thing worse than suffering is suffering alone. Twenty million Americans live alone, but feeling alone is different than living alone.

Feeling alone can happen in two ways. First, there may be no one there for you. Or second, you may be unable to feel the caring from those who are there.

Friendships are good for our health.[57] The kinds of friendships we have and the kinds of support they offer differ from person to person. The key is to receive the help we need. If you are already part of a community of people who care for each other, you are fortunate. If you are not, you may want to think consciously about how you can get the assistance you need.

There is no doubt that feeling like you have support helps when you are ill. What does having support really mean? It means not feeling completely alone. It means having someone you can call on for day-to-day help, at least occasionally. It means appreciating the support you are getting.

It also means learning to ask for what you need. And it means learning to recognize what you need, so you can ask for it. It means understanding that your physical needs are only part of the help you need. We need people to encourage us, to challenge us and to be our companions.

Recognize the support you are getting

There are very few ideal families, ideal neighbors or ideal friends. Yet as imperfect as they may be, people do care. You need to recognize that some are just better emotionally equipped than others to express that caring.

People are also very busy. In this day and age, most people live pretty hectic lives. Both parents work. Children are in at least three planned activities a week. Many adults are caught in the so-called sandwich generation, raising their children while caring for elderly parents. Can you recognize what support they are able to convey?

🍃 *Beth did call to express her regret that she hadn't been able to be more supportive. Her weekend trips to be at the side of her dying father (an eight hour drive, one way) were taking what little time she had, over and above a demanding job and a growing family.*

Can you remember that your friend visited six times after your last operation, or are you focusing on the fact that she has only sent a card this time? Could it be she is in a time of her life when the best she can do is send a card? Maybe she needs a card from you.

If you are feeling neglected, rejected or left out, it is easy to forget what support has been offered. It's support if:

- The kids empty the dishwasher.
- The car got cleaned.
- The doctor called back in reasonable time.

- The pharmacy delivers prescriptions.

- You were able to watch your favorite television program without interruption.

- Someone picks up your kids after ball practice.

- The neighbor cuts your lawn.

- Someone drives you to an appointment.

- A person sincerely asks, "how are you?" even if they have little time to listen.

- Someone takes on a role you had to give up.

- Someone holds open a heavy door for you when you are shopping or shuffling.

- Someone brings you a book even if you have read it before.

The choice is ours. We can focus on the support we are getting or the support we are not getting. Both deserve our attention. The issue is which one runs our emotional world.

Recognize that not everyone will understand

How can a woman know what it is like for a man to wear a catheter for three weeks? How can a superb athlete understand what it is like not to be able to play even a short game of ball? How can a person of 20 know what it is to lose your children and your legs in a car accident? They can't. Depending on their upbringing and experience, the best they can do is to express their regret and compassion.

If you believe people should understand, be prepared to be frustrated at times. Human experience is a teacher. If a person hasn't had the experience, they may not have learned the lesson. As Shakespeare said, "He jests at scars who never felt a wound."[58]

Even if people have had a similar experience, it may have been very different for them. If someone makes unrealistic comments or requests, you know they have not been where you are, even if they have had somewhat the same circumstances. They are not you. They don't necessarily value what you value, enjoy what you enjoy, or feel what you feel.

❧ *Helen, a counseling intern, looked earnestly at her supervisor when she tried to explain the dilemma. "How can I really know what they are feeling? My patient, Eric, just told me that when the nurse says 'I understand' he feels like his heart turns to stone."*

She went on, "I can't presume to have walked in their shoes; I haven't lived their story. My experience may not be enough to bridge the gap between our understandings. What scares me is that if I cannot truly understand their suffering, can I ever really understand their hope?"

Helen sat quietly. Then a smile broke out in her Irish eyes with the words, "I better not start with saying, 'I understand.'"

Could you have really understood someone else's circumstances, before this happened to you?

Be prepared for unsolicited advice

It's amazing to observe who feels competent to give advice. Like armchair spectators to a hockey game, these people think they know just how you should pass the puck. They believe they are flawless coaches, yet they don't even own skates.

Some people give advice because they believe they have been there. They declare, "Boy, do I know pain. I broke my ankle once. I was in a cast for three weeks." Some are control freaks who think you should do what they say because they know best. Others are self-righteous folks who know God would never do this to them. Each has his or her own version of:

"Well, if you would just do this..."

One of the least welcome directives is, "You'll feel better if you stopped doing so much." Toni's reply to this one was, "I am already going so slow my coffee is cold before I can get it into my mouth. And they want me to do less!"

The world is going to provide you with a few of these folks. You have options. You can pay attention to them, or you can:

- Tell them you have too much nausea to talk to them today.

- Ask them to get you the bedpan.

- Use the frustration to justify your comfort food.

- Imagine them walking away from you in your mind.

- Or, if you have the emotional energy and you feel cranky, you might want to say: "Harold, I am going to give a good deal of thought to what you have said, and when I write my memoirs, I am going to report it in the chapter, "Unhelpful advice I have gotten." If you are *really* cranky you could say, "Gee, Harold, you have me confused with someone who wants your advice."

If you use the last two suggestions, be prepared to tell Harold later that you were on a lot of pain killers and that you hope you didn't say anything inappropriate. To avoid the apologies later, simply save the rude remarks for you personal enjoyment.

Some "unwelcome advice" cards:

> **Thank you for
> your unsolicited advice.**

> **A scientific study has recently found
> that a hug has three times the
> therapeutic value of unsolicited advice.
> Thank you for one-third of a hug.**

> **I can hardly wait till you have
> what I have. I will come to your
> bedside and give you the advice
> you just gave me.**

Put your own message here:

Tell your story

Care of the soul... must begin with the simple telling of her story.
—Thomas Moore[59]

Talk it out. Paint it out. Keep a personal journal. In whatever is your way, tell your story. The value of getting your thoughts and feelings out is well established.[60,61] Telling our story in some form helps us get it in perspective, and it helps us to know ourselves in relation to the situation.

Self-help books and psychology texts don't talk about it much, but one of our strongest needs is "to be known," i.e., to have the world know who we are. Self-disclosure in whatever form it takes can be both healing and painful. We revisit old hurts as well as reconnect with our good memories. Unfortunately, on occasion, someone may judge us or attempt to correct our particular rendition of the story. Sometimes we really don't want a discussion. We just want someone to listen. We want to be heard or seen. We want to be known for who we are, not edited like a poorly written essay.

Is there someone who would listen to your story without judgment, without interruption? Select wisely. It takes courage to ask someone to listen. It isn't something we commonly do. It doesn't have to be a close family member or friend, or even a professional. It just needs to be someone who will truly listen.

When we tell our stories, we learn to revise them. You can tell them in various versions. Tell your story in the doomsday version. Then tell your story so the present is bearable. Perhaps also, tell the best-possible-outcome version. Remember you can tell your story in various mediums. Words are not the only way to tell it. Making a quilt, a painting, or a carving can be equally healing.

Notice, too, how you might alter the story depending on who is listening. It's okay that your story varies slightly depending on who is listening. The version we tell our children may vary somewhat from the version we tell at the office. It is our right to select which parts of our story we want to share with each audience.

Talk to someone who has "walked the walk"

To be ill is often to be "an emblem of peoples'
fear or an object of their admiration."
—Susanne Skubik[62]

The wonderful thing about talking to someone who has walked the walk is they know you are neither an emblem of fear nor an object of admiration. They know you are just someone who is struggling to make sense of life and to adjust.

If you want your hope boosted, talk to someone who has your condition and is doing well, if not physically, then in terms of his or her emotional and spiritual well being. Your doctor, friends, or a support group can usually locate one. As you talk with them, that little voice inside will start saying, "Yes. Yes. I feel that. I worry about that. I can see that."

If possible, try to find someone whose lifestyle is similar to yours. It makes talking easier. At Hope House, we have found that even people who have different conditions but who have some other common bond often find they get strength from talking to each other.[63] For example, a teacher who has multiple sclerosis may have faced similar things emotionally and have more in common with another ill teacher than he or she does with another MS patient who is from a very different line of work.

Make an agreement with this person that you can ask them any question, and that they can decline to answer it if they prefer not to. This way, you are free to ask personal questions and they are free to set limits on what they share. For example, men with prostate cancer and women with breast cancer can use this as their opportunity to ask someone who has already dealt with sensitive and important questions, such as "What changes involving intimacy and sexuality occur following surgery?"

You can only reach out in this way once you have decided two things. First, that you have an illness or challenging condition; and second, that just maybe others who have dealt with it for years could have something to offer you. A strong streak of independence is a wonderful thing. Yet it can also be a hindrance if it keeps you from reaching out for someone who could help you.

As you become a long-term survivor of your illness or condition, you in turn might help someone else by sharing your experience and story with them.

Attend a support group

❦ *"And I mean, people were telling my story. People I had never met before. I never found anyone who really knew what I was going through before this. And that just kept me there. I saw people who were getting better. I saw people who could have joy in their lives again. You know, they were okay with their bodies. And it gave me so much hope that if I did what they had done, I, too, would get better."*[64]

Support groups are a place to meet others who have walked the walk. As you listen, you will hear part of your story in theirs.

Although not everyone is a group person, you don't have to be outgoing to benefit from a support group. Either way, it has to be your choice. Can you imagine how successful Alcoholics Anonymous would be if anyone who drank too much was forced to go? The dynamics of a support group are based on the fact that everyone is there voluntarily.

There is a large body of evidence to demonstrate the value of support. Attendance at support groups has been linked with increased self-esteem, less anxiety, fewer symptoms and even extended life. Women with breast cancer who attended a support group and who were followed in a ten-year study conducted at Stanford University lived nearly twice as long as similar women who didn't attend a support group.[65] Heart patients as well have been shown to benefit from professionally guided and self-help support groups.[66, 67]

Support groups are a source of information. There will be people there who know the best Internet addresses, who will photocopy material they have found helpful, who will know where to get the special diet items you need, and who have opinions about the strengths and weaknesses of particular physicians.

It is important to choose a group that helps you feel better. Every group has the potential to be an "Ain't it awful" group or a "Together we can do it" group. You have to judge for yourself what will be helpful to you. You don't have to jump right in. Attend several times and then make a decision.

How do you find a support group? You can ask your physician, inquire through a help line (they have different names in different centers), call a self-help association if there is one for your condition, ask other patients, phone a medical center that treats your condition, put an ad in the paper, ask the resource center or librarian at your nearest large hospital, or let your community health center know you are looking for one.

If you can't find one, starting one is quite a challenge. However, a first step might be as simple as asking two others who have your condition if they would like to have coffee with you.

When they ask, have your list ready

You will hear: "I wish I could help. Is there anything I can do?" Be ready for that moment.

Aunt Mary can't drive for you. Cousin Fred shouldn't cook for you (or for anyone, for that matter!). The church ladies can pray, and they also would willingly provide some casseroles. If you want emotional support, don't call Jim. He would be better at fixing the garden hose that the dog chewed through. Betty and Carol would be terrific at buying your groceries. Dawn could do some of the yard work. Tom could pick up drugs, since he works close to the pharmacy.

Try to identify what you need and who can help by making a list like the following:

What are your needs?
- Food preparation
- Change dressings
- Get groceries
- Pick up the kids
- Buy a gift
- Get to the treatments
- Keep the yard presentable
- Get my hair cut
- Clean the laundry
- Do the banking
- Argue with the insurance people

- Companionship
- Return an overdue book
- House cleaning
- Get the kids to their activities
- Arrange a birthday party for Joey

Who is around to help?

Don't be too quick to rule someone out. Most people will be happy to do something small. If they feel they are not going to be responsible for a large part of your care, they are more likely to risk getting involved.

The whole idea of help depends on your ability to ask. Most of us have pretty heavy duty programming against asking for help. Inside of us, we hear a voice saying, "Don't be a burden."

To reduce the sense of being a burden, it helps to have a list of people who are willing to be on your team. Ask people in advance, "Would you have some time during the week after my surgery?" or, "I am going to be in treatment for three months. I am trying to work out a team that could help in some ways. I was wondering if you could spare an hour a week to help me." It soon sorts out the well wishers from the helpers. You might as well know early who is who.

> Eileen, a single parent with advanced breast cancer at 38 with a 10-year-old daughter, decided to reach out to the very few people in her world. With the help of a counselor she gathered eight people in her apartment and told them her dilemma. Together they identified all of her needs. At the end of the evening there was a volunteer or strategy to match every need. Someone would take her daughter once

every other weekend. Another would do her banking. Someone else would arrange for volunteer drivers through the local cancer institute. Yet another would see that she had unlimited quarters to do the added laundry that the nights sweats of chemotherapy caused.

Keep a job jar

People like to feel competent, so most will be willing to help. It is a lot easier for them to help when there is a specific task to do. When people say, "If there is anything I can do, just let me know," that's the time when the job jar helps. Every time you see something that needs doing, write it down on a slip of paper (or on a recipe card if you are fussy) and put it in a jar. People can whisk through the cards and see if there is anything that they have the skills to do.

Include household things: empty the dishwasher, water the flowers, re-pot a plant, fold laundry. Yard things: cut the lawn, sweep the steps, paint the fence. Lifting-the-spirit things: a little drive in the country, a flower on the table. Shopping things... The list can go on and on. You will be surprised how many of these tasks can be done without imposing on people for more than a few minutes of their time. Here are some more:

- Pick up a video.
- Fix the garden hose.
- Drive Julie to skating lessons.
- Pick up the bottled water and lift it onto the cooler.
- Be a substitute dad at the Scout banquet.
- Wrap and take a small gift over to your elderly mom at the home.
- Pick up thank you notes and stamps.
- Take the dog to the vet.
- Clean the fridge.
- Clean the windows.

This way, no task is too big. Just an hour here or there. You would do it for them, wouldn't you?

Remember, there are people, who for various reasons, may have to say "no." That's fair. Be prepared to accept "no." Be prepared to have people do tasks when it is convenient for them. Meanwhile, in the interim, look at the undone tasks and tell yourself, "I have arranged for that. I am in management now. I don't do the work. I arrange for it to be done."

If you like a sense of control, a job jar might make you feel worse. It might just remind you of how much there is to do, and that your home isn't tidy. A list will accomplish the same thing but it isn't as much fun as a job jar. You could, however, think of this as a special time in your life, unlike any time before or after. During this time you have received special permission and it is all right to ask for help, all right to do things in any order, and all right not to get everything done. You might want to keep that attitude even after you get well.

Ask your family how your illness is affecting them

Illness does not happen only to an individual. It happens to the whole family. Routines change. Expectations shift. Obligations have to be redistributed. Everyone, not just you, has feelings about the imposed changes.

You are not the only one who may be discouraged with your condition, afraid of the future, anxious about the results of a medical test, interested in an upcoming treatment, annoyed with the health care system or exasperated with the well-intended but insensitive neighbor who incessantly visits too long. You are not the only one who wishes you were able to do more for the people you love.

How do families talk about illness? At one extreme is the family that has made a health condition the focus of much of their conversation, indeed the center of the family's life. At the other extreme is the family where no one talks about the challenges that everyone is facing. Instead they just slam the door, and when someone asks, "What's wrong?" the reply is, "nothing."

It is important to acknowledge the challenges a family faces due to an illness. It is important to talk about those feelings—if necessary, with professional help. It is also important to remember that everyone has a life apart from the condition. You can let family members know that you remain interested in their day-to-day lives by asking:

"What went well for you today?"

If the answer is negative, just listen. You don't need to fix their world. Just hear out their ups and downs. Remind them of their strengths. Remind them they have a right to have a "down" day, too. Remind yourself that you are not responsible for how they handle things.

Learn to change the topic

Even the most compassionate people don't really want to hear the particulars of your catheter care. If things are not going well or nothing positive has happened since they last spoke with you, many people don't know what to say. It's best to simply share the highlights and move on.

Experiment with answers to, "How are you doing?" Give very short versions. "Encouraged." "Discouraged." "Hopeful." Then see if the listener picks up on particulars. If not, move on. This is not the person to whom you should bare your soul or show your dressings. In addition, there are only so many times you want to tell the story. If you tell it too often, you might find yourself focusing on your condition and inadvertently narrowing your own world.

A simple tactic is to say, "I am doing ...." (and a two sentence medical update). Then add, "I really miss (gardening, photography, theater, whatever)." This will give you the opportunity to talk about something interesting and not necessarily related to your illness. As well, it gives the other person a chance to talk about something out in the world that they can relate to and tell you about.

Mufty invented the world map strategy:

Mufty was admitted to the Montreal Neurological Center knowing she would be there for an extended time. She was determined her worldview was not going to become limited to the four walls of her hospital room. Creatively, she requested a large world map and a bag of pins. There was an incredible array of people from many nations working in this world-renowned setting. Each visitor identified his or her country of origin on the map, and the map became the focus of interest for caregivers and well wishers. Mufty says, "It wasn't exactly a hobby, but it sure saved me from all the 'Isn't it awful' gloom and doom conversations."

Avoid negaholics

Just plain avoid negaholics.[68] Have call display on your phone. Just don't pick up the phone if you think that talking to that person will be an effort. If you don't have call display, use a message machine and screen your phone calls. Learn not to give excuses for not calling back. When you get well, you can apologize for your rudeness. Negaholics:

- Whine.

- Tell you about the person they knew with your condition and how they died a terrible death.

- Itemize the lousy stuff that is happening at work.

- Berate your doctor.

- Imply that no matter what you are doing it isn't enough.

- Are chronic faultfinders.

- Keep you from trying new things so you won't be disappointed.

- Herald disaster with every paragraph.

Think of the people in your world as a garden. It is weeding time. At least for the time being, weed out the people who sap your energy. Cultivate life-giving people, people who:

- Are good problem solvers.

- Are fun to be with.

- Don't feel they have to talk all the time.

- Have a way of letting you know you are still important in the world.

- You feel good being with.

For the time being, consider yourself allergic to negativity.

Become deaf to negativity

If anyone says anything negative, let your unconscious hear it as if it is Greek, unless of course speak Greek, in which case Norwegian will probably do.

Some people, including health care professionals, are unaware of the impact of their communication. Strangely, sometimes ethics requires health professionals to focus on the negative. Prior to receiving chemotherapy, for example, you will hear about all the side effects whether you want to or not. It is required for "informed consent." Whether one can ever be fully informed about the adventure that is about to befall them is another question.

Relatives and friends also can inadvertently share the dismal side of life. Their version not uncommonly comes in the form of, "I knew someone who has what you have." If the tale unfolds that the person they know is now fully recovered, that helps. However, when they feel compelled to share with you that the person died a lingering death consumed by all the ills of Job, your psyche needs mental and emotional armor to deflect the potential wounds.

Doom stories have a way of infiltrating into our thoughts. When they do, exorcise them immediately. Try to say them in a foreign language, and you will smile.

Smile at strangers

Smile. You never know what can happen.

- *One day when I was feeling particularly low, I shuffled up to the table and chose the chair that looked into the wall rather than out to the other customers. I ordered salmon, not really caring that it was more expensive than I could afford. It was about the only thing my stomach could tolerate. A young couple was seated next to me. I looked like death warmed over. Caved in cheeks. Hollow eyes. Ribs showing through my summer T-shirt. I smiled at them, sensing their curiosity and discomfort. They smiled back. They added, "Not feeling so well?"*

  I replied, "Not doing so well."

  They offered, "Would you like company for lunch?"

  Thus began a long and supportive friendship.

- *On another occasion, there were two patients waiting when I entered the doctor's waiting room. The chairs were straight-backed and close together. The table was covered with an array of magazines. A slender woman of about forty was intent on convincing a younger, overweight woman of something. As I inadvertently eavesdropped, I heard her encouraging words, "Yes, you can be well. I was once as sick as you were. You have to do some things for yourself. The doctor can't do it all..." The litany continued with little response from the other patient, but I was hooked. I wanted to know this woman.*

From across the room I smiled gently each time she looked my direction. Sure enough, she initiated a conversation. Or did I, with my smile? She turned out to be a wonderful source of information and personal support for the same condition that I have.

❦ *Leonard was a small-framed man. Not so much short as lean and angular. With a mop in hand, he took his time as he cleaned the outpatient area. It was there that the cancer patients waited to see their doctors prior to their chemotherapy treatments. It was often a long wait in this narrow hallway crowded with patients whose eyes seldom met. That there were no windows down that aisle seemed like a metaphor of the whole situation. Leonard was custodial staff. Or was he? He believed he had two jobs. One was to clean. The other was to bring a smile to those who waited. Chair after chair got deliberate attention until Leonard's infectious smile and manner brought a smile. On to the next person.*

Smile back at the Leonards of the world. Mufty suggests using what she calls "The Six Foot Law":

Say "Good morning" (afternoon; evening), to anyone who comes within six feet of you. This is a policy for Royal Bank employees—but it really works just for life too! I do it in the locker room at my fitness center and have had some great conversations because of it.

Smiles really are contagious. "Smile and the world smiles back at you" is more than just a saying. Will everyone smile back? No. Men are a little less likely to smile and are less likely to be smiled at.[69] So, if you are male, you might want to intentionally experiment with smiling a bit more.

Young or old, male or female, well or ill, smiling is inexpensive, non-fattening and has no adverse side effects. You don't need a prescription, or even a reason.

Who could you give an unexpected smile to today?

Reflections on Support

- ♥ *From whom are you getting support?*

- ♥ *Who do you wish could provide more support?*

- ♥ *About whom is it best to lower your expectations?*

- ♥ *Who really just doesn't "get it"?*

- ♥ *Who would listen respectfully to your story?*

- ♥ *Have you talked with someone who has "walked the walk"?*

- ♥ *With whom could you really level about what's going on?*

- ♥ *What support group could you attend, even as a visitor?*

- ♥ *If you were to attend a support group, what group might it be? How would you find it?*

- ♥ *Where will you keep your "job jar" and the list of people who can help?*

- ♥ *What are three topics to which you could practice switching conversation?*

- ♥ *Is there a negaholic in your life? Who would you prefer to spend time with?*

- ♥ *How long since you have smiled at a child you didn't even know?*

Emotional Health

Consider your emotions messengers

Many of us are raised to hide or dilute strong feelings. We hear:

- "You don't hate your sister," or

- "You're not that sick," or

- "It doesn't hurt now, does it?"

Can you imagine a time when, rather than being afraid of crying, cursing or cowering, you were actively curious about the intense feelings you have? It takes time to learn to decipher emotional messages if you are unaccustomed to the language of feelings. Most of us are more comfortable with some emotions than others. We feel okay with anger but not with sadness. Or, we can cry easily when we are sad or upset, but we don't know what to do with guilt.

Feelings have no power in themselves. They simply announce the needs of your internal world. Whether you are gripped by fear, overwhelmed by guilt, stressed from overload, hungering for love, raging with anger or despairing with sadness, the emotions themselves are messengers. What are they trying to tell you? Try to discover what they are asking you to pay attention to.

Meet adversity

At some point you have to choose.
You shift to hope or you drown in despair.
—Mufty Mathewson

In the midst of emotional turmoil, physical pain or financial ruin, we seldom want to hear, "You'll be a much stronger person for this," or, "God never gives us more than we can handle." Few people have the inclination to say, "Yes, I'm sure my character will benefit so much from this." Adversity doesn't work that way. It is painful. It is real. It holds no assurances of benefit. Surviving it requires hope.

How we meet adversity crafts us into the people we are. There are those who come to understand Nietzsche's famous statement, "That which does not kill me, makes me stronger."[70] As we surmount challenging circumstances, we acquire a certain veteran status. It builds our confidence when we realize we can handle challenges. Increasingly we are able to say, "This, too, shall pass." We learn we can handle the difficult stuff, despite the fact we would prefer not to have it in our lives.

Name those fears

If you are ill, there is a good chance that somewhere in your situation there are some fears. One way to face these fears is to name them. After you do that, then you can decide if you want to do anything about them. Sometimes fear diminishes simply by being acknowledged. Here are a few common fears.

I am afraid:

That I will lose my job over this.

That the treatment won't work.

That my friends won't accept me.

That my spouse will leave me.

That my kids will have memories of me as a "sick" mom.

That I will bankrupt the family.

That I won't be able to handle the pain.

That I have no future.

That I will die.

That I won't die.

Now check today's reality:

I have seven weeks of sick leave so I have time to plan.

I am already halfway through my treatments.

Mark visits less often. He often whined anyway.

My wife is weary but we do love each other.

The children have adjusted well. They play at the neighbors.

We have 15 percent less debt than we counted on.

I have good pain control.

I am alive.

I have hope.

Which fears are really scary? Real or imagined, fear is like oil on a rug. It will creep further and further into your life unless you restrict it. What help might you want with your fears? *Feel the Fear and Do It Anyway* by Susan Jeffers is a good introduction to managing fear.[71] Talk it out. Write it out. Work with little pieces of it. Decide not to give it your life.

Following a serious illness in 1978, every mild symptom I experienced was accompanied by doubts about my ability to handle another serious round of the condition. Like many a veteran, as the years passed, I began to recognize that fear is as much an enemy as the actual condition. Fear was the thief. A veteran learns that the condition is not the sole enemy. Fear, despair and doubt take their toll. The war is won, battle by battle, one hill at a time, as hope triumphs over despair—if, at times, only by a fraction.

Years later, when recurrence threatened my quality of life and pain again took its toll, fear lurked at the edge like a vulture, ready to devour what it could of my life. One day in front of the mirror, a pain furrow etched in my forehead, I looked at myself and spoke assertively as if to inform another person of a non-negotiable decision, "I may have to live with pain again, but I do not have to live with this fear."

Assign someone to do your worrying

❧ *I was awaiting major surgery. I had lost 35 pounds, was feeling like hell. There were lots of things on my mind. How would the surgery go? What would they find? How would I manage afterward? What would I do with all of my obligations? What if I couldn't eat after? What if I had to have an ostomy? Would I have to be on medications with heavy side effects? What if? What if? What if?*

All of those "what ifs?" are worries.

Mufty called. She is a wonderfully mature women in her sixties who, with her delightful spouse, Bill, has raised four children, faced most of life's adversities and casts her optimism and love widely in the form of personal support and leadership. Mufty offered to do my worrying. "My worrying?" I asked.

"Yes, your worrying."

"Are you serious?"

"Dead serious."

"Do you have to use those words?" I joked. But she persisted.

"I will do your worrying. Give me a list of what you are worrying about."

And I did. I equate this to the buying of warts. It is said that if someone buys your warts they will disappear. Well, Mufty took my list of worries and I ceased to have them. Whenever the concerns would revisit, I would tell myself, "No need to worry. Mufty is worrying about that." When I would develop a new worry, I just called Mufty. She and I usually would rate them from 1 through 10. I still call Mufty on occasion and inquire whether she would be willing to worry for me.

Who could do your worrying for you? You might be surprised who that someone is.

Try it out and see.

Forgive yourself

Guilt has little value. So you smoked cigarettes, even though you knew the risks. Or, maybe you got stressed out over the finances. Did you let yourself get dangerously overweight? Practice unsafe sex? Did you travel in Asia against your Aunt Mary's advice, and sure enough, get sick? Well, if so, these things make you human. If they can't be reversed, they can't be reversed.

If you have done harm to yourself or to others, it's human to feel guilty. The real burden of guilt is not being able to let go of it. Guilt gets heavier over time.

One way of thinking about guilt is to think of it as a 100 pound stone you carry. It may be time to put it down. If you can't let go of it all, perhaps you could lessen the burden by carrying less. How heavy is your stone? How light would you let it be? How willing are you to carry less, or even nothing?

Guilt is about the past. Well-being is about the present. Is there something you would like to learn from the past? If there is, great. Acknowledge the lesson. Change the behavior, minimize the damage (physically, emotionally, spiritually) and get on with life. If you are blaming yourself for something, sure enough others will, too. If you forgive yourself, others are more likely to.

Guilt can interfere with seeking help. Then later, when the condition has worsened, you add on *more* guilt for postponing getting help. It is important that you seek help from a professional who won't add to that guilt, who is willing to focus on what can be done, rather than what you should have done 15 years ago. If you find yourself with a "You brought this on yourself" caregiver, tell them that you are already very good at guilt. Now you are working on forgiveness.

Stop playing the "blame game" and insist that others stop playing it, too. Start today. Seek out the help you need from whoever can provide it for you. Increasingly, professional caregivers understand that forgiveness may be part of helping you to gain a sense of well being.[72]

Forgive yourself.

Recognize you are angry

The signs are subtle at first. Your voice has an edge to it when you say, "Please put away the groceries—now!" You don't want to explain yourself. You just want obedience. If you can't control this frustrating disease, you want to control something! You don't want to be controlled. You want the channel changer in your hand.

Other signs of anger may be that you find yourself irked at the incessant advice you receive, despite good intentions, or that loud noise becomes a personal affront. Maybe being jostled in an elevator becomes an invasion of personal space. You might find yourself using more addictive substances—i.e., cigarettes, alcohol, chocolate, drugs—or even work. You may be asking why people are driving on *your* road; seeing *your* doctor; or spending *your* tax dollars on low priorities. You are sure you are right; and you feel almost equally sure you are powerless to make the right things happen.

Just below the anger is the fear that you have become insignificant. That you can't make a difference. That your life is being stolen without your permission. Of course you're angry!

Some people truly seem to have a nature that does not include being angry. Most of us, however, would have to admit to experiencing some version of anger. We are *irked, frustrated, irritated, upset, furious, mad* or *enraged* at some point. A first step to dealing with anger is to acknowledge, "I am angry." For instance, "I am annoyed that there are delays in my treatments, frustrated that I can't lift things, irritated that the kids don't seem to know that I am tired, mad at the world for being an unfair place, enraged at being told it's all in my head." Being angry is a normal reaction when our world is not the way we want it to be. Anger does not have to be based on something visible or even logical.

Becoming aware of your anger puts you more in control of it. Then you have choices about how to express it. It won't spill over unexpectedly in inappropriate situations. If anger was unacceptable in your upbringing, you could start with just acknowledging it to yourself, even simply by whispering it out loud. A trusted friend may listen, too. You don't have to yell to let people know you are angry.

Remember, anger has a value. It is like a red light warning us something is wrong. It can indicate what you may need to grieve, or change, or simply talk about. First, though, comes the recognition.

Don't wait for an apology

On occasion we might know why we are suffering but we want the responsible party to say, "I'm sorry." A communicable disease? A needless accident? It wasn't your fault, yet you bear the consequences. Somehow an apology would help immensely, but it is simply not forthcoming.

Justice is part of hope. It is easier to go on when we feel the unfairness has been acknowledged and dealt with in some way.

Yet, how long can you afford to postpone physical or emotional healing? Is it worth waiting for health until the responsible person is able or willing to say, "I'm sorry"? Sometimes it can take years to get an apology. Sometimes it never happens. Are you going to let them injure you more deeply by keeping the wound raw?

Use your anger creatively

Of the seven deadly sins, anger is the most fun.
To lick your wounds, to smack your lips over grievances long past,
to roll over your tongue the prospect
of bitter confrontations still to come,
to savor to the toothsome morsel both the pain you are given
and the pain you are giving back—
in many ways it is a feast fit for a king.
The chief drawback is that what you are wolfing down
is yourself.
The skeleton at the feast is you.
—Frederick Buechner[73]

Every family, every culture, and every person is unique in terms of how they feel, manage and express anger. Anger is a natural emotion that tells us something is not the way we want it. There is big anger and little anger. Our anger may or may not be justified in the situation. The fact that we may want something does not mean that what we want can happen, or even that it ought to happen. Either way, we need to deal with the emotion of anger.

The most constructive approach to anger is to identify its source and deal with the issue. What's making you angry? What can you do to change the situation? Finding the answers to those questions isn't always so easy. Sometimes you just don't feel up to it; you'd just rather be angry. Sometimes you're just not ready, or you may know that "this is not the time." If you need to avoid or deflect it rather than address it, see if any of these work for you. Let's use an example.

136

Having a hard time getting someone to end a visit or to stop coming to see you?

- Doze off in their presence.

- Be so cheerful, it puzzles them.

- Keep mentioning how many friends you have who are lawyers.

- Mention that your condition is contagious.

- If you suspect they are sucking up, tell them you changed your will. See if they keep visiting.

Got a bigger resentment? Try Betty's way. The week Betty had a mastectomy her husband had an affair with a family friend. Under normal circumstances, Betty was the epitome of graciousness. However, after recovering from the sheer shock and hurt, she gleaned considerable satisfaction from fantasizing spilling a drink on the mistress at an upcoming social event. Experimenting with different one-liners to accompany the spill deepened her confidence and lessened her anxiety about confronting the woman. When the event did arrive, Betty had the confidence to deliberately make her presence felt by graciously moving into the other woman's space. The relationship interloper left the party early.

Rage is a serious form of anger. Professional help can help resolve this type of anger. Think about how life would be if you were without anger. You don't want to stay distressed longer than necessary or, even worse, hurt someone else in a moment of rage. Remember, if you harbor anger it can shave years off your life. Use hostile styles for expressing your anger sparingly,[74] and get help to turn your anger into positive energy.

Ask for a "puppy"

🐾   *It was a long trip. With the airline strike and the flooding of the Rochester airport, it seemed getting home was yet one more hurdle. We had to go stand-by from Winnipeg to home. I tried to get comfortable, laid out across three airport chairs. It was after midnight. At 88 pounds and eight days out of surgery, I was weak. Very weak. I recall when the daughter of a young couple approached me with advice. In her assertive, five-year-old way she announced, "If you want to go to sleep, close your eyes real tight and don't open them." Her apologetic mother compassionately laid a lengthy coat over me and initiated a conversation with my mom about our journey.*

We did get on the next plane. At 3:00 a.m. the wheelchair rolled off the cargo elevator and I saw the joy in my father's eyes for the first time in several weeks. We were all tired.

The room I had known as a child was filled with sunlight when I awoke to the voice of my mom saying, "You have some visitors." My best friend slipped quietly into my room placing a large grocery size box on my bed. He tipped it slightly and out come seven wriggling puppies. Each had to discover their new territory. Each snuggled, sniffed and cuddled. And my hope grew a foot.

Ask someone to bring you a puppy.

Keep a personal journal

Journal writing is an age-old therapeutic tool. It is a way of confiding to ourselves. It clears the mind, helps us take in new ideas, fosters problem solving and creativity, and reduces trauma. There are avid journal writers who say that if you keep a journal you will never need a therapist.

For some people, keeping a journal comes easily. For others, the idea is enough to make them want to take extra pain medication. The first step is the willingness to experiment. You don't know if you are a person who would benefit from journal writing until you try.

How do you start?[75, 76] Select a journal in which to write. Some people like a hardback. Some people like coil bindings. Some enjoy using a special pen. Then find the time. Some people have preferences for writing in the morning, others at nighttime. There is no right or wrong way to use your journal. Journaling is not an assignment. No one is going to grade you. It is just yours.

Privacy can be an issue when you are ill. In the front of your journal write, "This is a PRIVATE and CONFIDENTIAL document," or, "Don't even think about reading this!" or both.

There are many ways of using your journal that will help you emotionally. You can:

- Write letters to real or absent people. Write to those who strengthen your hope or those who have bruised it.

- Engage in conversations with others, with parts of yourself or with issues. For example, have a dialogue with your health condition.

- Sketch or doodle what life would be like if you felt really well.

- Reflect on special moments.

- Make lists.

- Try writing a poem or create a special prayer.

- Record quotes.

- Remember humorous stories.

- Record your dreams.

- Assign yourself small problems and practice giving advice to yourself.

- Try this exercise, popularized by Oprah Winfrey, the talk-show host: she suggests that each day people write down five things for which they are grateful. Oprah calls this the "Gratitude Journal."

- Share with your spouse. Some couples keep journals in which they both write. If a pen is left in the journal, a response is requested. Sometimes writing can accomplish what talking doesn't.

Begin with a strategy that seems reasonable to you. Keep your journal nearby. Make entries when it feels right. Making it one more thing you have to do usually doesn't work. Do your best not to judge the value of what you write for at least a few weeks.

Check with your friends. You might be surprised to find that one or more of them has been keeping a journal for years.

Curse a little

My dad is Scandinavian. He has always claimed there is no satisfaction in cursing in English, it's simply too limited. Come to think of it, I have never heard him swear in English. Well, maybe once or twice but never the really bad words. The extra value of swearing in Norwegian is that it didn't contaminate his children. My mom used to tell him to say, "Ketchup! Ketchup! Ketchup!" He did seem to get considerable relief from a minute or so of good hearty cursing, particularly that time he struck the tractor tire with the hammer and it bounced back.

My mom didn't curse. She raised her eyebrows! She didn't have an alternate language through which to vent her frustrations. Believe me, though, the raising of her eyebrows, usually just the right one, was far more intimidating than dad's brief foreign ranting.

For the pure of heart, swearing won't make you feel better. It is simply too foreign to your being. However, for those of us who get to the end of our tether once in a while and want to let the world know, select an appropriate time, imagine you are auditioning for a part that requires you to be really obnoxious, mixing in some bad words and tones, and enjoy! If you can't bring yourself to say the words, substitute, *"Ketchup! Ketchup! Ketchup!"*

When you are finished, don't forget to tell yourself that the audition is over and it is time to go back to real life.

Flick the elastic

Sometimes in order to use emotions as messengers it helps to have a little extra reminder. Someone in the field of family therapy deserves credit for this technique.

Simply put an elastic band on your wrist. When you get into behavior or feelings that you don't want, flick the elastic and remind yourself to return to the present moment. Then say to yourself whatever you need to hear. It could be along these lines:

That was yesterday. Today is now.

I am not doing that anymore, remember?

Oops, forgot!

My apologies. Just had a moment when I slipped out of training.

What would I rather focus on?

Have mini-conversations

When you are weary, it is difficult to muster up the energy to talk about what is bothering you or even to share what you may be enjoying. With people you know well it isn't necessary to have long in-depth dialogues. Sometimes the context of what you are meaning is embedded in a few words because both of you understand the situation. By sharing a few words, you have the satisfaction of a full conversation. Listen in on one. These two people know exactly what they mean. They can have an abbreviated discussion with ease.

Ed: *"Dorothy?"*

Marg: *"Concerned?"*

Ed: *"Difficult time."*

Marg: *"For the kids, too."*

Ed: *"Harold?"*

Marg: *"Home Tuesday."*

Ed: *"Fun?"*

Marg: *"West Edmonton Mall."*

Ed: *"Grandkids too?"*

Marg: *"Bobby?"*

Ed: *"Bad fall."*

Marg: *"Hockey."*

This is not just a few single word or phrase interactions. They know this technique and use it purposefully. Listening in, we are unable to fully understand the range of the discussion they are having. But they do!

Try a mini-conversation. It can be fun.

Let the tears come once in a while

The old adage, "Sometimes a good cry helps" is probably true. Crying is a way of "washing your soul."

Some people worry that they might never stop crying if they start, or that they might fall apart if they allow themselves to cry. Others say, "What's the point?"

You will not cry forever. Most people can't keep it up for 20 minutes. You might be the exception and make it to a half an hour! Many people tell of feeling more composed, calmer, even stronger, after a good cry.

If you want practice, be around a small child. They inevitably cry often, then arise from the ashes of their trauma and eat their cookie. Cry along with them. Be prepared for them to look at you strangely.

Try different styles of crying. If you are not someone who usually wails, give it a try. You might be surprised to find you do it well, or you might find yourself laughing at your effort.

Walking in the quiet of nature is one of the best places for a good cry, because you won't be interrupted. Crying is hard to do if you have to perform with civility at the same time.

As long as our souls are filled with despair there is no room for joy. Crying makes room. Nothing more. You will not feel worse, nor will you fall apart. Crying just doesn't work that way. If you are truly afraid of what will happen if you cry, cry only with someone you know can put you back together.

When engineers design a dam, they always build in a floodgate, so when the pressure of the water behind the dam becomes too strong and the integrity of the dam is threatened, some water can be allowed to flow out, taking off the excess pressure. Perhaps the human body was designed with tear ducts for similar reasons! What's the point of crying? Tears are floodgates for the body, psyche and spirit! Try it and see.

❦ *Milton had suffered almost unbearable sinus pain for three years. Medical tests showed no physiological reason for his chronic condition. At his doctor's suggestion, he sought therapy.*

It was not long before the topic of the murder of his only child brought on tears. He had long feared that if he ceased to be the "rock" he had been for his wife that he would disintegrate from despair. He felt he could not begin to allow it to take over his life. He decided he could not allow himself to "dwell" on the pain.

As a result, before this Milton had not shed a single tear. When they finally came, they came as deep, wrenching sobs. Over time, the tears and rage began to lessen. A month later, Milton was free of sinus pain. He had been healed by his own tears.

Slow down

Feeling overwhelmed? Your body may be asking to do less. Take your "To Do" list and:

smear it with peanut butter,

put it on the lawn

and watch the birds peck away at it!

Seek the counsel of a professional

Are you one of those folks who think that only "disturbed" people ever see a professional for counseling or advice? Is it okay to talk to your physician or even your clergy, but you wouldn't want to be seen in the office of a psychologist, psychiatrist or social worker? For some people, seeking help from those who are trained specifically to help with emotionally intense situations still carries a stigma. However, the very same people have no difficulty seeking counsel from a financial consultant, using the services of a travel agent, bringing their computer in to a specialized repair shop, or hiring a ski coach.

Confident, skilled help is available. It is perfectly acceptable to ask about the credentials of someone you are going to use as a consultant to your life. Various professional organizations also have referral services that can assist you in finding qualified help.

Reflections on Emotional Health

- *What is one fear that you know you need to face?*
- *Can you name three honest fears?*
- *How do you usually handle fear?*
- *Who could do your worrying?*
- *Is there anyone who you wish would say, "I'm sorry"?*
- *For what do you need to forgive yourself? What would be the first step?*
- *What is your way dealing with anger? What would one alternative be?*
- *Where could you experience a puppy?*
- *What will be your code words for cursing?*
- *Would you prefer a plain blank book or a fancy, hard-backed journal?*
- *What could the elastic band technique help you change?*
- *What color elastic band are you going to use?*
- *With whom could you experiment with abbreviated conversations?*
- *If your tears could speak, what would they be saying?*
- *Around what activity have you allowed yourself to feel pressured this week?*

Simplifying Your Life

Keep out the clutter

*I will join you in protecting us from the clutter of life and negotiate
with you times and events that temporarily unbalance our lives.*
—from the wedding vows of Ronna Jevne & Allen Eng

*My life cannot implement in action the demands
of all the people to whom my heart responds.*
—Ann Morrow Lindbergh[77]

*Learning the difference between what I wanted and what I needed was
the hardest lesson I ever learned... and the most worthwhile.*

Illness is a time of added demands. However, it is also a time when we have less energy, fewer resources, and fewer options. Under these circumstances, simplicity is a useful rule of thumb.

What in life can we make simpler? Shopping? Relationships? Day-to-day activities? There is value in getting your priorities clear, streamlining your routine, uncomplicating your physical world and cleaning your emotional and mental storage rooms. Where would you like to begin?

The shift to a simpler life begins with a decision. Often during a time of extra demands we are tempted to apply the "additive model." That is, we just keep adding tasks and activities, assuming if we go a little longer, a little faster, somehow we can keep things *normal*. Would you be willing to acknowledge this is *not a normal time*, and it is okay to introduce changes that will simplify your life at many levels?

Be a few casseroles ahead

❦ *Cathy, our daughter, leads a demanding life. She works full time, is a farm wife, shares the raising of three teenagers and has her own health concerns. She's a six-hour drive away. She couldn't come at the time of the operation but she did something equally as supportive. She brought a cookbook that lays out complete menus for a month and provides an accompanying grocery list. The first afternoon, the groceries were purchased and laid out on the counter and table. The celery got cut. The chicken was diced. The onions were peeled. The next morning the cooking began. By the evening, we had cooked enough casseroles for a month. Pastas, fish dishes, stews, a few we would consider specialty items. For days after we came home, weary from what was a challenge far beyond our expectations, at every mealtime we would say, "Thank you, Cathy. Thank you, Cathy," and open the microwave door.*

If you know you are going to be laid up for a while, lay in the casseroles. One-dish versions are best. If you don't have a daughter like Cathy, friends will help. Have them label the casserole dishes. Tell them, "Simple is good." Be sure to tell them if you have any dietary restrictions or preferences. Have them make them in the size that you need. If you are not in a situation where you know people who could do this, find a church that has a visiting team. Someone might be willing to organize the help. Most people don't fully use their freezers. If you don't have one or if yours is not big enough, a friend or neighbor may let you store dishes in theirs and you can bring things over by the week. You might find an occasional dish missing, but then what are friends for if they can't share?

There are now many "month at a time" cookbooks you can purchase or get from your library.[78,79] They are organized so that the grocery lists and food preparation are efficiently matched. They offer a good variety and, for just one day's work, the result is one month's worth of meals, already prepared.

If you can't get hold of a cookbook, make two of everything for a while. Freeze the extra one. If you don't cook, photocopy this page and send it to three people who do, or put it in your job jar!

A few suggestions that an average cook can prepare include:

salmon loaf	chili
soups	stew
chicken and rice	spaghetti and meat sauce
lasagna	macaroni and cheese
shepherd's pie	tuna casserole

Shop by mail, phone or Internet

Books, clothing, household goods and gifts are all available by mail order, phone or Internet. You don't have to venture into the crowds. Sure, you might miss a sale or two, but you'll save by avoiding impulse-buying. It can be quite enlightening to browse catalogues. They are a study in anthropology. In a store, I might not see the electronic tie rack for men, or the doormat that talks. I have also noticed that catalogues have a greater selection of moderately-priced items than I see displayed in the stores. Maybe they are there in the stores, but the advertising draws our attention elsewhere. By shopping from home, you'll save physical and emotional energy that you can use for activities that yield greater satisfaction.

How do you get the quality catalogues? Begin by asking friends. They will each have a favorite.

Television shopping has its risks. Impulse buying can happen when high powered sales people trained to convince the viewer seem to be talking directly to you right in your living room. If you are going to do shopping on the Internet, become informed about security issues first.

Whatever the medium for shopping, the idea is to simplify the activity rather than complicate it. The goal is for it to be convenient without having to sacrifice quality.

If you actually really enjoy shopping, check with the local department stores. Some have special arrangements for people with disabilities or for seniors' shopping. In some areas, stores actually close their doors to the public to accommodate shopping for those without the usual benefits of good health.

Want to go on a *small* shopping trip? Make an outing to a card shop. Plan on that being the only thing you are going to do, other than to get a frozen yogurt or cinnamon bun. Have with you a list of everyone whose birthdays, anniversaries or graduation is coming up in the next three months. Buy the cards. Maybe pick up a "Get Well" card, too. Someone is always getting ill these days!

Simplify your physical care

❦ *At under 50 years of age, there seemed to be a certain irony being taken to the mall by a woman of 76. I knew I would be tired but I also needed to know there were still people in the world. And I hadn't had a haircut for four months! I just didn't have the energy. Onlookers would be hard pressed to have picked out which one of us was the senior. We went to one of those places where you can see what you would look like with different hair styles. You come away with photographs of your best possibilities. Normally I would be resistant to spending money on such "entertainment." But I needed a lift, and I got it. And people love my new hair style. I look younger and it is easier to keep up.*

How can your physical care be less demanding?

- Stop buying things you have to pull over your head.

- Buy shoes with Velcro instead of laces.

- Put a chair right beside the entry door, so you can rest as soon as you arrive home.

- Get a little stool for the kitchen to make reaching easier.

- Clean your closet. Anything you haven't worn in three years goes. You have been keeping it when someone could be using it. Take it to a consignment store for resale and enjoy the found money, or take it to a thrift shop and enjoy the fact that someone else is going to appreciate it.

- While you are at it, clean out your medicine chest. Outdated or partially completed prescriptions from previous times, go. They can actually be dangerous. Most pharmacies will dispose of the drugs for you. If you are not well enough to do so for yourself, add it to your job jar. Someone may choose to do it for you.

Restrict visitors

Some people are blessed with many friends and acquaintances. Trying to see them all or even to write the thank you notes can be exhausting. People do understand. Most just want you to know they care. They can handle someone saying, "John will be up to seeing people in about three weeks."

❦ *The operation didn't go well. None of the parade of visitors stayed long or demanded much, but cumulatively they were draining me. Finally, Carol posted a sign at the door: "Dr. Jevne is conducting personal research into the benefits of uninterrupted rest. Please leave your card or well wishes at the desk. Thank you."*

Later, the surgeon agreed to discharge me only if I agreed to, "No visitors for six weeks, except your elderly father!" He announced that he knew a workaholic when he saw one, because he was one as well.

What would your sign say?

Own a message machine

Wendy was weeks in intensive care following a devastating motor vehicle accident. While she hovered between life and death, her parents' energies were directed at being at her beside. At that time, her mom wrote:

The phone seems to never stop ringing. The calls are essential to us but we have little energy to return them. We have a new telephone answering machine so, each day, we put an update of Wendy's progress on the machine. People soon understand they will not be troubling us and will be getting the latest information about Wendy by phoning.

When we get home from the hospital we are renewed and revived by the many messages of love, hope, help and prayers. We have no phone calls to make. We never feel alone or abandoned. There are friends wanting and needing to help as close as our telephone machine.

The messages we leave on our telephone answering machine keep track of Wendy's progress. They are snatches of the most intense, powerful, emotional, exhausting ten weeks of our lives. ...We record the messages we leave and of the people who call.[80]

A phone message machine does not have to be something you dread the moment you walk into your home. It could be a source of strength and good wishes in a difficult time. Your message might include something that lets people know you are not able to return all the calls, but that you do appreciate the support.

Go for a getaway

The geographical cure sometimes really helps. Being away from the day-to-day hassles can give you a different perspective on things. Getting away takes energy so it usually has to be planned. It doesn't have to be for long. Try not to travel at peak times or to busy places. Perhaps a friend has a cabin that you and someone could visit. If you can get to someplace in nature, go. Even a view of a harbor or a garden will do. Check into a hotel or motel in your own city. Then watch the eyebrows rise!

If you can't actually travel, go there in your mind. Ask a friend if they could bring you a travel video from the library. Better yet, if you can handle it, go to the library for a brief outing. It's quiet. There is lots to read. And no one can phone you! When someone asks you later, you can say you were looking up something.

Pick your battles

The dishes are in the sink. The peanut butter is always on the counter, never in the cupboard. The newspaper is late. The doctor hasn't phoned back. The neighbor's dog barks incessantly. Your physical therapist isn't very encouraging. The Book Club keeps sending you a bill for a book you never received. Your aunt keeps sending religious poems with hints that if you were a believer you would be cured instantly. The back door sticks so badly some days you have to go around to the front. You are paying the youngster down the street to cut your lawn, but it looks like a buzz saw ran away on it.

Do any of these sound familiar? Researchers have found that daily hassles affect people's lives as much as, if not more than, major life events.[81] Whenever you don't feel well, you have only so much energy. Where do you want to use it? Which things are worth being hassled about? The peanut butter jar? The back door? Yes, they are all annoying. Do you want to spend what little energy you have being annoyed? If you could be annoyed about only three things (okay, four) which ones would be worth your energy?

1.

2.

3.

4.

What could you do with the other ones? Ever thought of using photographs? Photograph the mess in the kitchen. Put the pictures on the fridge with a little sign that says, "Want me in a better mood? Try putting things away." Don't forget to acknowledge the first sign of your family's efforts to please.

Repeat after me

Have you got a cluttered mind? Things go around and around in your head. You go over worries that little can be done about. You rehearse conversations that are already over. You tell yourself you shouldn't feel this way or that way. You make one decision and change your mind three hours later. You think you have your priorities set, and then they get unsettled! The last adjective you would use to describe yourself mentally would be "quiet."

Our minds are complex mechanisms. Sometimes it can feel like your mind controls you, rather than you control your mind. It can feel like there is a voice inside you that will never let you be. Junk thoughts are like junk food. They are not good for us. It can take practice to discipline our minds to move to a quieter, simpler place; to replace that internal voice that is always agitating us with a voice of confidence. "Self-talk" is a common way of turning up the volume on the inner voice that can help us simplify our lives, emotionally and mentally. We need to practice thinking thoughts that will help us.

Often the unhelpful thoughts are about the past or the future. If we can get into the present, life becomes more manageable. We can become more focused on what is needed, what is possible, and what is available. Here are some pep talks that people have found helpful:

I am feeling a bit down, but I have been here before.

I am going to stay in the present. There is something I can do now.

I don't wish to make myself feel worse. I am, to the best of my ability, going to interrupt my negative thoughts.

I will take "baby steps."

Being anxious or down is pretty normal for my circumstances. I have not failed because I am not always positive.

I can relax. I can breathe more deeply.

I will pay attention to my feelings and do my best to understand what they are telling me.

This is not the worst that can happen. I can cope. I may need time, but I can cope.

I can ask for help. I do not have to do this alone.

Clean your mental closet

Mentally we can torment ourselves by self talk about what we *should* be doing, how we *should* have acted, what we *should* be able to control. Not only does the body need a break from "shoulds," so does the mind.

When someone is hassling us, we often respond using the expression, "Give me a break!" Well, that's what the mind is saying when it feels overwhelmed. "Give me a break!" You can choose to listen. It works to everyone's benefit if you respect the request before something actually breaks—like your sense of humor or the relationship with your son.

Your mind can get cluttered with all sorts of obligations and responsibilities that are inappropriate for the situation in which you find yourself. Life becomes simpler if you clarify what you have control over and what you are responsible for. Once you have that clarity, you can use the elastic band technique to remind yourself that this is simply the way things are these days.

To start, sort out what you have control over and what you don't have control over.

Complete the following sentences:

- I have control over...

- I don't have control over...

Then sort out what you are responsible for:

- I am responsible for...

- I am not responsible for...

Practice it out loud:
"I am not responsible for..."

Take a sabbatical

A sabbatical is a period of time when one is relieved of the usual responsibilities in order to concentrate on other goals. Sabbaticals can be wonderful things. It is a chance to say, "I will be gone for a year so I need to resign from these committees." It clears the deck.

Consider taking a sabbatical from the obligations in your life that are not absolutely necessary. During your sabbatical, your goal is to get as well as is possible. Any activity that depletes your energy, goes.

Not everyone is involved in community service or has multiple memberships in this and that. Some because they have no interest. Others because it takes up resources. If belonging to organizations or activities gives you a great deal of enjoyment, the question may be how can you minimize the energy you use on them while continuing your connections. Or, you might even want to take a leave of absence for a year. What would be healthy for you?

How many things do you belong to that you really don't need to during this period of time? This may not be the time to be on the library board, the parent teachers' association (not even the phone committee), or even the Bible study group. If it feels like an unwelcome obligation, this is not the time to be participating. It goes. It only stays if it is life-giving to you. When you feel better you can dazzle people with your wellness by getting involved again. Meanwhile, from what would you like a sabbatical?

Think about it: If you have two hours of energy a day, how do you want to use them? If your answer is "I want to attend the council meetings and protest the freeway"—then go for it!

If not, do what you need to do to remove yourself from obligations. Do yourself the extra favor of dealing with any pressure by well-meaning others to keep you a "part of things." Let them know that your decision is to withdraw from the activity. Let them know that it wouldn't be good for your health to stay marginally connected and that you are looking forward to the possibility later. In other words, let "no" mean no. The joy and freedom of a sabbatical will soon replace any regret or guilt.

Break a little rule

❧ *Struggling to cope with newly-diagnosed diabetes, low energy, constant infection, hypoglycemic bouts and general life demands was just about doing Donna in. She was trying to keep up with all the normal responsibilities of life, while simply adding new self-care duties to the load. The stress was pretty well canceling out the benefits.*

She decided she needed to pamper herself. How could she do that? She needed to break some rules, let go of some of the "normal" expectations she had learned years ago as a child. The first thing she did was to stop making her bed. For nearly four years, she rarely had a tidy bed. She changed the sheets regularly but never spent that extra few minutes pulling blankets into a neat order and putting on a spread.

She couldn't believe the sense of freedom it gave her. That freedom carried on far out of proportion to the three minutes it actually saved her.

Rules are like preset software. They are the program by which we run our lives. Things have to run a certain way. At the time we develop the rules, they may work very effectively for us. They become habits that seem to make life work more efficiently, more effectively. Life seems simpler with rules. We know what to do and what not to do. Rules work well if we have the health, time and resources to live up to them.

Rules can be like glass ornaments, however. They aren't flexible. Unlike a willow, they cannot bend. When our circumstances change, our challenge is to reassess the rules we have been living by. Often this is more emotional than we realize, for until then, the rules have provided us with routine and safety. This is the way things have been done. This is what we have come to expect of ourselves. It is not easy for many of us to embrace doing things differently. Yet, if we did, we could simplify our lives during a demanding time.

Do I really need a garden this year?

Does supper really require having a dessert?

Do I need to host an office party?

Could someone else drive Jennifer to Brownies?

Could someone else mow the lawn?

Could I leave my bed unmade?

Forgive someone

*Once you choose to forgive, it's like a crack in the
wall, and a little bit of sunshine can come in.*
—Shann Ferch[82]

Forgiveness is invisible. It happens from within. It fuels the soul. It leaves us with a sense of being set free. Some have described it as a letting go. Forgiveness does not feel "logical." It may even feel unreasonable. Forgiveness is no small task when we have been seriously affected.[83-87]

Have you been deeply hurt? Do you find there is a situation that continually returns to your mind plaguing you with a sense of injustice?

Doris Donnelley, a theologian, suggests that there are steps to forgiveness.[88] Whether you agree or not, it is a starting point.

- *Acknowledge the hurt.* Admit that something or someone got to you and that you are not able to "snap out of it."

- *Decide to forgive.* Make an act of will for the spirit to forgive, even though you don't know how it will happen.

- *Remember, forgiveness isn't easy.* Real forgiveness feels like a little death. We are slaying the decision to exact revenge.

- *Forgive yourself.* We are holding ourselves in bondage until we can forgive the other person.

- *Consider the consequences of not forgiving someone.* A Chinese proverb puts it succinctly: "The one who pursues revenge should dig two graves."

Forgiving doesn't necessarily mean forgetting. It needn't mean accepting the person back into the central part of our lives. It means we open our heart again to the world. We inch forward again into the experience of risk.

Life is simpler with an open heart and an open mind.

Develop a hope kit

The future is uncertain. That is its nature. Until it becomes the present, it cannot be known. Planning for it does not ensure it will resemble our vision. The best case scenario is that our wish list will come true and our hopes will be fulfilled. What, though, if they are not? How will your hope be affected? Do you have a hope kit ready to survive a difficult time?

Every home and work place has a first aid kit for physical injuries. Why not a hope kit readied for unexpected adversity? Imagine that in 24 hours you will find yourself without a home, separated from your family, work will be irrelevant, and you may be physically threatened. None of this situation will be resolved in the near future. Create a hope kit to sustain your hope throughout this time of uncertainty. It must be small enough to carry. What could you possibly put in a such a space that would remind you that life is worth living?

Although you can create a hope kit in your mind, there is added value in actually doing it. The hardest time to prepare one is the day that you need it. When you think of what you would need to sustain your hope, what tangible reminder could go into the kit? Maybe a mirror—so that every time you lose sight of hope, you could reflect light into a dark spot. Maybe a cocoon—to remind you that metamorphosis can lead to something beautiful. Maybe a photo of your grandmother—because she believed you could do anything.

See if you can think of the rationale for including some of the items others have suggested:

175

A can opener (to open minds)

A hammer (to build community)

A calendar

A cartoon book

A special letter

A candle

A compass

A key

Sweet grass

A photograph

A small strong thread

Is your hope kit packed and ready to go? Is there someone in your world that needs a hope kit? You could start one for them.

Reflections on Simplifying Your Life

- *What is the clutter that makes you want to say, "Stop the world! I want to get off"?*

- *What's your favorite casserole?*

- *Where could you get one mail-order catalogue?*

- *If you were to dress simply today, what outfit and shoes would you wear?*

- *What are three things in your closet you haven't worn for three years?*

- *What limits would you like to place on visiting these days?*

- *What is the funniest message you have heard on an answering machine?*

- *Where could you go to "check out" for at least four hours?*

- *How could you arrange a hassle-free day?*

- *From what might you resign?*

- *How could supper be simpler?*

- *From what would your mind like a break this week?*

- *How would your life be simpler if you forgave someone for something?*

- *What little rule would you like to break this week?*

- *What is the first thing you are going to put in your hope kit?*

Your Spirit

Take care of your spirit

Spirit is the "invisible companion of the body."
—Deepak Chopra[89]

We can get along without our souls for a little
while in life, but not for long.
—William F. Lynch[90]

Recently there has been a resurgence of talk about spirituality, about finding and expressing our real self. The writings of authors such as Thomas Moore have popularized the need for "care of the soul." Bookshelves are replete with new age spirituality gurus informing us of the pathway to our enlightenment. Mainstream religion lifts an eyebrow, but there is no denying that we are talking more about our "spiritual" life than a decade or two ago. Angel boutiques and celestial music are evidence of a growing interest in another realm. Millions tune in every day and join Oprah Winfrey for her segment on "Remember Your Spirit."

We speak of someone's "spirit being broken," of someone "not being himself," of a piece of writing or art as "having no soul." We understand something of the spirit in the way things are offered or taken away. We understand what it means to have put "your heart and soul" into a project. Other references have become ingrained in our culture, too. "We search for our soul or lose it... eyes are the windows of the soul... concrete jungles have no soul... we give our souls up to God... we break our hearts but we lose our souls... soul mates long to live together."[91] We have soul music, soul food, and soul-murder...

Defining spirit or soul is nearly impossible. Let's leave that to the theologians and the philosophers. What we know is that each of us has some sense of when our spirits are low. We know when we have a fighting spirit. We know when we are "okay" on the inside and we know when we are not. We need to be as committed to taking care of our inner being as we are to taking care of our body.

Taking care of your spirit may be something you have not talked about before, or perhaps it is something you have never even thought about. However, we do need to be able to ask ourselves, "How am I? Really, how am I? How am I... on the *inside?*" Just as your body needs to be nourished, so does your spirit.

Thomas Moore suggests, "care of the soul does not have the goal of making life problem-free, but to give ordinary life depth and value."[92]

Because your body is ill, your spirit doesn't have to be ill also. If you are going to keep your spirit alive and well, it is a conscious choice to do the things that comfort and strengthen it. What is good for my spirit may be different than what is good for yours. There is a general rule of thumb, however. Whatever we end up doing needs to be something that makes us feel closer to feeling like the person we know we are. We have all heard the expression, "I am just not myself today." It is our way of saying that something about our spirit needs a lift.

Our spirit is an amazing part of us. It acts like a signal system. When our spirits are low we can presume there is something missing. Just like our bodies get hungry, our spirits also need nourishment.

Recognize you have a spirit!

How unique are we? I teach personality theory to graduate students. One of the ways to make theory come alive is to apply it to actual people. For one project, several clients had written biographies. At the time, they released the writings as case studies for educational purposes. They worked hard to remove any identifying data from the writings. Even though they seemed less concerned than I about such issues, we had had an outside person read them for hints of any identifying material.

Despite these conscious efforts to disguise the person of the biographical case studies, one of the readers approached me at the break, commenting, "I think I know this person." She believed the person had been in a grade seven classroom with her for a few months. She could not articulate what "exactly" it was that made her think it was her junior high classmate. It just felt like it was her. Indeed she was correct, despite a twelve-year gap since the last contact. The person had left a lasting image.

In a similar way, an artist develops a signature. It isn't just the name in the corner of the painting. There is something about the paintings, such that even if they weren't signed, we would know who painted it. There is something unique about them.

Think for a moment. What is there about you, that would make you or others say, "That's just like Mike?" (or whatever your name is). If you are not sure, ask someone. Whatever it is—a sparkle in your eye, a propensity to organize things, your soft-spokenness—it is a reflection of your spirit.

By acknowledging that "yes, I have a spirit, something that is uniquely me," you can more consciously take care of it. Deny it, and it will just pester you until you do. If you continually say you are fine when you are not, you will pay a toll. If you are unwilling to grieve the future that cannot happen, your spirit will remain sad. If you lose the ability to do something and pretend it has no effect, your spirit will change. Your spirit will do whatever it can to signal to you that you need to take care of it, this important part of you that is invisible.

Return to nature

*A garden exists not only as part of your backyard landscape, but
as a site that resides in your imagination, a collection of personally
satisfying images that can be expressed upon your land. A garden is
as much a state of mind as it is an actual place.*
—*J. Moir Messervy*[93]

*All through the long winter I dream of my garden. On the first
warm day of spring I dig my fingers deep into the soft earth.
I can feel its energy , and my spirits soar.*
—*Helen Hayes, Actress, 1900-1993*

Nature is full of hope. A fawn suckling a doe. A fledgling learning to
fly. A pale pink flowerbud that blossoms. The dawn that follows night, and
the promise of a new day. The tender green sapling that becomes the oak.
The stream that becomes the river. A flood that restore nutrients. The
changing seasons.

Gardening is a way of having a miniature version of nature right in our
own environment. We can marvel at the wonders of a seed maturing into a
blossom, feel the cool earth, watch the creatures great and small come
nearer, and enjoy the products of our labors in a fresh salad. No wonder
gardening has become one of the most popular pastimes! It needn't be a big
garden. The healing value of gardening can be experienced by everyone,
from seniors to the mentally ill, to stressed-out caregivers.[94-98]

Sunlight is no small part of the importance of nature. Seasonal affective
disorder is a form of depression, sometimes severe, that results from
insufficient exposure to sunlight. Our bodies need natural bright light.

185

Although you may live in an urban environment, how can you get into nature? Some areas have handicapped-access parks designed for people for whom regular parks are ill-equipped for outings. Some have community gardens where people who don't have yards can rent plots of land to plant vegetables or flowers. Yes, it takes planning to get to those special places. But it is important to visit them.

Keep a flower in a vase

If a man finds himself with bread in both hands,
he should exchange one loaf for some flowers.
—Mohammed, the Prophet, 570-632

It is no accident that when we are unwell people send flowers. There is something life-giving about them. They are both fragile and beautiful. William Wordsworth was well known for celebrating the specialness of flowers. In his poem, "To the Small Celandine," he notes that we often have a flower that is special to us.

Pansies, lilies, kingcups, daisies,
Let them live upon their praises;
Long as there's a sun that sets,
Primroses will have their glory;
Long as there are violets,
They will have a place in story:
There's a flower that shall be mine,
'Tis the little Celandine.[99]

Bouquets are lovely, of course, but they often accomplish no more than a single blossom, reminding us of the landscapes momentarily outside our vision. You just need a little one. And it doesn't have to be store bought.

Say a prayer

Everyone prays in their own language.
—Duke Ellington[100]

Every prayer is an expression of hope.
—Henri Nouwen[101]

Whether or not you practice a faith, within or outside of a religious community, the body of evidence supporting the value of prayer is impressive. What is prayer? Perhaps it can be described as a touching of hearts, a communion of spirits, the passing of caring from one to another. It is the reaching out for the Holy, as we recognize the holy in one another. It cannot necessarily be taught. "To offer the world instruction about prayer would be impudence," C.S. Lewis once said.[102]

Physician Larry Dossey has brought to attention the expanding body of evidence of the power of prayer. He concludes,

> *There is great mystery here. By "mystery" I do not mean temporary ignorance that later will be swept away by additional information, or questions that will someday be resolved by future research. I mean mystery in the strongest possible sense—something unknowable, something essentially beyond human understanding.*[103]

Evidently, there are over 20 kinds of prayer.[104] I am not sure if God designed it that way, or if someone very tidy just needed to straighten out and label the prayer cupboard. There are prayers of petition, intercession, confession, lamentation, adoration, invocation and thanksgiving, to name just a few. You don't need to know all those classifications. All you need to understand is what your heart is aching for.

Maybe you want to ask for energy to get through today, or for a friend to visit. You might just want to spend some time thinking of your blessings and being thankful, or in adoring God in gratitude for a beautiful day or a special experience. Or, perhaps your heart is heavy and you want to cry out in despair and anger. God is there to hear those things, too.

Perhaps the mystery of prayer has to be experienced. There are more aspects and dimensions to life than we can understand with our limited intellects. Words are somehow inadequate to convey what prayer can mean in your life. Over and over people do say, "Through prayer, I am never completely alone."

Is there someone you care about, for whom you want to offer a prayer? Even if you're flat on your back and can't so much as turn a light switch off or on, you can pray for someone else who is in need today.

Write letters to God

Your letter can be short, long, proper or even a mite disrespectful. God will understand. God understands how rare it is to be listened to, so expect full acceptance of your anger, confusion, despair, hopes and joy. You don't need to mail them.

I'm serious. You need pen and paper. You might want to use good stationery considering to whom you are writing. Using a fountain pen seems to suggest you are taking extra consideration as well. Yet, as far as I know, jottings on the back of napkins are equally acceptable to God. You can write as often as you want.

If your energy is low, it is also acceptable to create the letter in your mind. Think about where you would want to be while you write this. Do you have a favorite place where you could feel safe enough and comfortable enough to share what you would really like to say to God?

Letters to God can be light or serious. They can be brief and personal, like this one (found circulating on the Internet and e-mail):

> *Dear God,*
>
> *So far today, I've done all right,*
> *I haven't gossiped, lost my temper,*
> *been greedy or grumpy, been nasty,*
> *selfish or overindulgent.*
> *I am very thankful for that.*
> *But in a few minutes, God,*
> *I am going to get out of bed.*
> *And from then on, I'm probably*
> *going to need a lot more help.*

Dear God,

I expect You are pretty busy and you don't have much time to read mail. But I have been wondering something and it seems to me You're the only one who can give me the answer. Why did you choose me when You were handing out the cancer?

I mean, in the big picture, I understand that we all have to die to keep the world from getting overcrowded, and each of us is eventually going to die of something. But I had plans, you know? And some of them just might have helped You make the world a better place. I was going to be a board member of the YWCA, sponsor a foster child, spend more time with my daughter and bring joy to my grandchildren. I was going to take skiing lessons and learn to crochet and overcome my fear of heights. Now, instead of doing these things, I am waiting for tests, waiting for results and trying not to worry my family.

I really think You should have chosen someone else! Any chance You might reconsider?

Dear God,

I got confused today. I started to wonder why I even try. The setbacks are so frequent I feel like the man in the myth whose eternal punishment it is to roll a boulder to the top of a hill, only to have it roll right back down again. It is hard today not to feel like a victim: a victim of the disease, a victim of our fast-paced society that devalues ill people, a victim of a cosmic joke that singled me out but kept from me the reason why I am being tormented.

Help me to accept there are many mysterious things in life. Help me to understand that I have a well of strengths I have not yet tapped. If You could send me a sign that there is something worth staying alive for, it would really help. I will do my share and keep my eyes open for the evidence.

...And would You mind hurrying?

❦ *Gerri had had a long winter, with chemotherapy and radiation. By spring, she was exhausted and weak. She decided on a vacation in Florida. In the early mornings before the burning sun came out and the crowds descended, Gerri would wander on the beach. In a quiet cove, each day, she wrote a letter to God, in the sand. In her heart, she believed that as the waves lapped at her message and took it out to sea, it would reach God's heart.*

Say "thank you" often

That's it:

Just say—

Thank you,

Thank you,

Thank you!

After a while, it comes naturally.

Give in some days

Tired of fighting? Of coping? Of having a stiff upper lip? Do you feel like giving up? Do you have goals in your head but they all seem like they would take too much effort? It's time to "opt out" for a day. Call it a "getting ready" day, if you prefer. It is a day when you are getting your body and soul ready to continue the good fight. Even good soldiers have to pull off into the ditches in order to rest and prepare for the next battle.

This is the day to:

Cancel obligations

Do jigsaw puzzles

Watch the soaps

Have a drink—of whatever

Lose yourself in a crossword puzzles

Flip the channels 20 times an hour

Take the extra pain medication

Read the comics

Remind yourself, though, that this is a "Give-in" day, not a "Give-up" day, and that you will regenerate. This is not a permanent state of mind. It is a necessary break.

Give yourself a "Poor Me" day

A "Poor Me" day is a day when you are allowed to say, "Poor me." You don't have to be logical or reasonable. You don't have to be specific to your illness.

You don't really want to do this alone. It helps to have someone listen. It is key that they not interrupt or try to make you feel better. They might even say, "Yes, poor you!" at your request.

On a "Poor Me" day you also are allowed numerous indulgences!

Here are a few of my favorites:

Poor me, I can't eat what others eat.

Poor me, I have to go to another medical appointment.

Poor me, I get tired so quickly.

Poor me, all the rest of my family is well.

Poor me, I don't get the visitors I want.

Poor me, I can't draw.

Poor me, I never got ballet lessons like my cousin did.

Poor me, I have never written my novel.

Poor me, I have to work for a living.

Poor me, my insurance plan doesn't pay for everything.
    (This is not the day to be appreciative that you even
    have an insurance plan.)

Poor me, it always rains on my days off.

A "Poor Me"day can be very therapeutic. If a day is too long, feel free to adjust the length of time. A "Poor Me" hour is sometimes sufficient. If your partner or caregiver needs some "Poor Me" time also, negotiate not to take it simultaneously!

Choose life

Many of us believe that there is a point at which we would not want to live. We ultimately have that choice. Perhaps, though, it is best that we not have a predetermined, inflexible point in time where we would call it quits. As we face advancing symptoms or limits, it is remarkable how we can modify expectations and discover unused strengths.

> ❦ *Everybody, well or ill, imagines a boundary of suffering and loss beyond which, she or he is certain, life will no longer be worth living. I know that I do. I also know that my line, far from being scored in stone, has inched across the sands of my life: at various times, I could not possibly do without long walks on the beach or rambles through the woods; use a cane, a brace, a wheelchair; stop teaching; give up driving; let someone else put on and take off my underwear. One at a time, with the encouragement of others, I have taken each of these highly figurative steps. Now I believe my limit to lie at (my husband) George's death, but I am prepared to let it move if it will. When I reach the wall, I think I'll know. Meanwhile I go on being, now more than ever, the woman I once thought I could not bear to be.*[105]

It can be difficult to give an unequivocal "yes" to life. Sometimes we truly feel we want to say "yes" only "if things turn out," "if the treatment works," "if the kids are okay," "if I can stay financially afloat," "if I don't lose my ability to walk." "If, if, if..." In reality, saying "yes" to life can be decided and redecided each day.

I have noticed that once a person firmly decides for life, despite what challenges it offers, something often changes for them. The question changes from "under what circumstances do I want to live?" and becomes "how am I going to deal with this difficult situation?"

What do you need to face the challenges? Do you need more adequate pain control? Someone to talk with? Do you have a plan for handling those weak moments when death seems like the only open door? If you feel especially vulnerable, keep the phone number of a crisis line close by.

Find the still point

Our minds are amazing. Ever notice how you can be thinking of a dozen things in just moments? How will you get to the doctor's office, how much will the drugs cost, will your son come to visit? It goes on and on like chatter in a endless, random soliloquy. It has been called our monkey mind.[106] This unbridled outpouring of thoughts takes us from the past with its "what if's" and "remember when's" and into the future with its worries of catastrophic tomorrows and its dreams of a blissful future.

A *still point* is a quiet place in our minds where the chaos and activity of everyday life is exchanged for a sense of solitude. It is like the eye of a hurricane. The storm can continue around us, yet we feel powerfully safe at our still point. There is no denial of the storm; nor is there a need to directly encounter it.

It is not so much a physical place we go to, although that is also a possibility. A special park bench. A quiet pond. A favorite café. However, it is more accurately a place in the heart and mind that allows our deepest self to be at peace. For some, it may be triggered by a memory or recollection, often of a place where they have experienced peace. When you are in your still point, you feel like you are being held. There is no fear, just peace.

If you know someone who seems to have that "peace that passeth understanding," talk with them about still points. Exchange ideas with your friends about how or where you might find your still point. You can also read more about still points in *No Time for Nonsense: Getting Well Against the Odds* (by Ronna Jevne and Alexander Levitan, and published by Lura Media).[107]

Celebrate the mystery

Life is more than a to-do list. It is an amazing gift and is worthy of being celebrated every day.

You needn't wait until you feel well or healed to celebrate the day-to-day joys. Why not openly celebrate?

Send a friend a card.

Phone a grandchild.

Start a gratitude journal.

Hold an orange and marvel at it.

Watch a goldfish.

Go to a butterfly garden.

Close your eyes and listen to a favorite piece of music.

Lie in a canoe and drift with your eyes to the clouds.

Watch an infant put his toes to his mouth.

Watch a three-year-old child eat a pickle.

Read the Psalms out loud.

Put a candle on your grapefruit!

It doesn't always have to be serene and logical.

Create a mandala

"Mandala" is the Sanskrit word for "circle," but a circle that is coordinated or symbolically designed so that it has meaning for us.[108] To create a mandala for yourself, draw a circle. Then think of the different parts of your life. Attempt to create some sense of what is at the center of your life and how it relates to the rest of your world.

Use the space below to sketch your mandala. Borrow the kids' crayons or felt pens and actually color it in. Once it feels like it represents something meaningful for you, think about making a larger version of it. You could paint it, quilt it, carve it, or make a placemat of it. It's up to you. Lie back and see if it begins to take shape and form.

Sing the blues

Give yourself over to music—homemade or purchased. Invite it to soothe you, invigorate you, excite you, release your tears and your rage. It can be the catalyst for feelings which might otherwise go unexpressed.

Try singing out your worst fears in the shower. Sing them in dramatic opera, or mournful folk. Pinch your nose and add a country and western drawl. Nothing gives voice to chronic pain more powerfully than a real hurtin' song. You can howl in between the verses.

❧ *A woman was asked to play the organ at the funeral of a loved-one. Having never played at a funeral before, she worried that she might not do well, and hurried off to practice at the church. To her surprise, the practice became her greatest comfort and she gave it more time than she had intended. Tears dripped onto the keys. In solitude, she played and she mourned. On the day of the funeral she was calm and professional.*

Revisit the music you collected when you were young. Turn on the stereo and play the old songs that make you sad, and have a good cry. If anybody asks why you're crying, you can say you were listening to sad music. Find some protest songs from the sixties and rant along with the singers. Turn off the stereo when you've raged enough.

Ask yourself what songs might remind you of hope. If none come to mind, ask your friends for songs that remind them of hope. You might zero in on a piece of music that would inspire you to victory if you were going into battle, or in this case, will marshal your immune system in preparation for surgery.

Don't forget to connect with playful music, too—the silly kind that makes you giggle. This giggling is an expression akin to joy. Recall your old camp songs. Sing a few verses of "Great big gobs of greasy grimy gopher guts," or "Found a peanut, found a peanut, found a peanut last night." Ask others to recall silly songs they once sang. Silly songs are much sillier when you sing them with others.

If your thoughts are silent, let music be your voice. Nobody likes a whiner, but people will pay big money to hear a croaky rendition of the blues. [109]

Each night, look up at the moon

🍏 *It was hard knowing our son didn't even know both of us were ill. He was somewhere in India. In his four years away we had heard regularly by phone or letter how things were and where he was at least every three months. It was now nearing six. Several of our letters had been returned. It helped somehow to know that the last thing we often said on the phone was, "Remember, each night we are looking at the same moon." Each night we would look out our bedroom window that permits a wonderful sky view. There it would be. The one thing in the world that connected us to our son.*

What connects you to someone you love? A grandmother's locket? Hold it while you drift off to sleep. A child's drawing? Frame it so you see it often. Find some way of knowing you are connected, and that you are loved.

Reflections on Your Spirit

- ♥ *What word do you use for "spirit"?*

- ♥ *How could you bring a little piece of nature inside?*

- ♥ *Have you a special vase for your daily flower?*

- ♥ *What is your way of praying?*

- ♥ *If you could post your letter to God, where would you send it?*

- ♥ *For what are you thankful today?*

- ♥ *Do you need a "Poor Me" hour or a "Poor Me" day?*

- ♥ *Have you said a firm "no" to suicide? Do you need to?*

- ♥ *What is one thing that makes the struggle worth while?*

- ♥ *Where and when are you closest to your still point?*

- ♥ *What's a favorite tune you like to hum?*

- ♥ *What will you do to celebrate today?*

- ♥ *What stage of the moon do you most like to watch?*

- ♥ *What colors do you see being dominant in your mandala?*

Living in the Present

Live today, look forward to tomorrow

❦ *A young mom was devastated each morning going into her son's hospital room. The pit of her stomach had never recovered from the news that seven-year-old Ben had leukemia. He had actually taken things amazingly in stride. He missed his school chums and he hated the pokes in his back, but he complained of little else.*

Each morning, she would brace herself as she neared his door. Bald headed, thin, seemingly losing ground, he was so young—just old enough to read the children's menu with those big blue eyes. As she stood in the doorway this morning, he glanced up at her with his contagious smile. Her whole heart smiled back.

"What's so great this morning?"

Bursting with enthusiasm, he hastily blurted, "Mom, they're going to have Fruit Loops for breakfast tomorrow! I love Fruit Loops."

What you have is TODAY

Few have captured the value of the moment as well as Patsy Barrineau in her book of poetry about the cancer experience.[110]

The Good Thing About Cancer

is that it speaks

in short sentences.

I listen attentively

as malignancy whispers:

Applaud yourself.

Hold his hand longer.

Hug her.

Buy it.

Say it.

Touch.

Kiss.

Smile.

Scream.

Laugh.

Cry.

Enjoy.

Live.

Yes.

Create a ritual

Rituals serve two purposes. They help us celebrate and they give our lives stability. Significant events in our lives are almost always marked with some form of ritual. Graduation, marriage and even death have their accompanying rituals.

Our daily lives often have rituals we hardly notice. We brush our teeth. We kiss our partner or children, or both! We watch the television favorites.

Some rituals we do alone. Some we do together. We join in the after-game festivities. We worship with members of our faith community. Some love the solitude of an evening walk, a predawn meditation or a morning swim. Some rituals become almost habit, devoid of meaning. Others do indeed help us notice that each day can be special.

Notice what rituals you already have in your life. You may be surprised that you also are practicing a few which do not contribute to your health. Create a daily ritual that gives you joy. It needn't be profound. It can be, but it needn't be. Likewise, get rid of a ritual that is unhealthy or negative.

One young woman who was fighting the discouragement accompanying unstable diabetes and the recent death of her mother decided she would dance for a minute or two each evening before going to bed. Her body loved it, and not uncommonly she would shed a tear, or delight in a giggle.

Each of us chooses the ritual that fits for us. Sometimes we specifically decide on an action, like the young woman above who dances. Others find a ritual that is developing in their lives and then they begin to cultivate it, as Mark has:

❧ *Mark was off work for months with his symptoms. He found the lack of meaning in his life as hard as the treatment regime. A bird feeder loaned to him by a friend was a turning point. Each evening at dusk he checked the feeder. Not long after he was checking the Romantic poets. Soon he was writing his own poems after ensuring the birds were cared for. The hard-backed journal, the old bench lugged over from the garden, and the ambiance were all he needed to feel a sense of quiet and meaning at least once a day.*

For the less artistic, I recommend consuming one cherry-filled dark chocolate about three o'clock every afternoon in honor of the day.

Forego the "yes, but"

The person who continually says, "yes, but" is canceling the future. It could be you. It could be the people around you. "Yes, but" is always seemingly logical. It may represent a perfectly sensible hesitation.

Yes, but I tried this before.

Yes, but my wife would never agree.

Yes, but it is too expensive.

Yes, but the food was cold.

Yes, but I am too old.

Yes, but it is so unpredictable.

Yes, but you are not an expert.

Yes, but I heard about a time when it didn't work.

Yes, but what would others think?

Yes, but it takes so much time.

Yes, but...

    Yes, but...

        Yes, but...

        Yes, but.

Try two experiments:

1. Refuse to say, "Yes, but," for three days.

2. Refuse to accept, "Yes, but," for three days.

Every time you want to say, "Yes, but" let yourself say, "I wonder how..." instead. It can also be helpful to experiment with exchanging the "but" with "and." Every time you hear, "Yes, but," experiment with asking, humbly and without a smirk, "I wonder if I could call upon you to be slightly more positive!" If they simply repeat, "Yes, but," you might suggest they remove their butt from your room.

Develop interests outside of your health

When you have a serious illness or condition, it is easy to become enthralled with your own "against all odds" story or "poor me" sagas. However, each of us needs a life beyond our illness.

If you have a hobby, great. Sometimes the hobbies we have at one point in our lives no longer suit our new circumstances. They have to be placed among our good memories and alternatives have to be found. Carl Hiebert, author of *Gift of Wings: An Aerial Celebration of Canada*, is an example.[111] Despite being a paraplegic, he has twice crossed Canada in an ultralight aircraft taking pictures and writing of his excursions. You needn't aspire to such an extraordinary achievement, but who knows what enjoyment awaits you?

What would you like to learn? With few exceptions, it is not too late to try new things. You don't have to become the whiz kid at whatever you try. It isn't about becoming "the best." It is about enjoying yourself and using time in a satisfying way. Many avid hobbyists got their start in unusual ways, beginning with a simple goal or interest.

  ❧   *When I met Joyce she was torn between bitterness and sadness. She had raised five children on her own. Now it was her turn for life. It was time for less obligation, a few extra dollars to pamper herself, the occasional unscheduled hour for leisure. As she neared retirement, she had developed a rapidly growing breast cancer. She was so angry. She felt so cheated. In her stubbornness she decided she would not die until she had knit each grandchild a sweater. At this point she had not knitted anything beyond 4 x 4 squares while helping a daughter in a home economics class thirty years before.*

Seventeen sweaters later, she was the envy of the chemotherapy room as she showed off her next project. Each sweater was unique. No two were alike and she had become increasingly sophisticated with the patterns. She wanted each sweater to take longer since she wasn't sure what next goal might help her stay alive.

What have you wanted to try? What would you like to accomplish? Are your golfing days over and your photography days beginning? Are you an avid hiker now thinking you might try aquacise? Did you enjoy pettipoint, and now have to think about crocheting? If you are laden down with "I can'ts," check to see if they can be turned into "I cans."

Get a library card

Pleasure reading is one of the most often identified enjoyable activities.[112] During 1991, 75 percent of women and 57 percent of men read a book.[113] Reading is nourishment for the mind. Your brain is like your other muscles. Use it or lose it. Research has shown those who read for pleasure may be significantly less lonely.[114] Here are some suggestions to get started:

- Ask people to share their favorite book.
- Let people know what kinds of things you like to read.
- You can get newspapers from libraries, too.
- Remember, books also come on tape.
- There are people who will read to you.
- Make your outing to the library instead of to a coffee bar.
- Think about whether there is anything you would like to know more about.
- Libraries often have special events.

It all starts with a library card. If you are in an area where library cards are free, drop a note to your local politicians expressing your appreciation. If there is a charge for a card and your finances are tight, ask for one for your birthday or put it on your wish list for Christmas. Ask the home care nurse. Get someone to get you a library card. Even if you don't feel like reading, take out *National Geographic* and just look the pictures, or just go to the library and watch people. Get the library card.

Volunteer

*It is said there is no limit to the amount of good a person
can do if he does not mind who gets the credit.*
—*Robert Fulghum*[115]

The value of volunteer time in the United States equates to $150 billion each year, making altruism one of the biggest sources of revenue for the United States' Gross National Product.[116] In Canada, volunteers contribute a total of over 1.1 billion hours of time in a 12-month period, 22 percent of the volunteers contributing over 200 hours a year.[117]

Volunteering is good for your health. A study following several thousand men discovered that those who did not volunteer were two-and-a-half times more likely to die during that time as those who did volunteer at least once a week.[118] Reductions in arthritic pain, lupus symptoms, asthma attacks, migraine headaches colds, bouts of flu and stress have been reported as benefits of volunteering.[119] Now, that is reasonably-priced insurance!

It is key that you *want* to volunteer. That's what volunteering means. It is something that needs to be within your control. Being obliged to volunteer doesn't do it! Lack of a sense of personal control undermines one's health. It is okay to be hesitant to try it, though. It may mean meeting new people or doing things you have not done before, and that can cause anxiety in some people. Whatever your motivation, if you continue you will be likely to receive the benefits—except of course, if you expect something in return.[120] Helping another with an open heart is part of the story of survival throughout history.[121]

If you are not up to volunteering, then use the channel changer to find a program about someone who does. It has been demonstrated that even watching altruistic service, for example, a film about Mother Teresa, can change the amount of immune agent in your saliva.[122]

If you were to volunteer, what would you want to do? Don't overcommit. There is some small task out there that you can manage. How do you find that task? Ask friends where they volunteer. Inquire about what they like or dislike about it. Ask if you could go along one day. Call the volunteer center in your community. They will have suggestions. Stop in someplace where you visit on occasion—e.g., a kindergarten, a seniors' center, a nursery (the flower and plant kind!). Inquire if they could use help in some way. Tell them what your limits are.

Want to feel good right away?
Rehearse an afternoon of volunteerism in your mind.

Take one small step toward being your new self

You have heard it a hundred times. It goes this way:

"How are you?"

"I'm just not myself today."

Sorry! That *is* the self that you are today. Imagine how silly the conversation would become if we continued it:

"Oh, I am so sorry. Who are you today?"

Healthy or unhealthy, we just don't stay the same person. No cell lasts longer than seven years. We grow several fingernails a year. Our skin totally replaces itself in every two years; our blood changes every fourteen days and difficult as it is to believe, we "rebuild" a new heart every thirty days.[123] Why would we expect to always be our "old self"? We can grow and adapt emotionally and spiritually, just as our bodies do. We can develop new attitudes, new friends, new strengths and new hobbies, but not until we are willing. Sometimes we don't know what we can do until the situation is thrust upon us. Dwelling on who you used to be doesn't help you get on with who you are *going to* be or *need to* become. Who knows, you might find you like your new self, too.

> ❧ *Janet's husband, Bob, died suddenly at 34. She and her three small children were devastated. She doubted she could ever recover. She wondered how they would survive. Three years later she was heard to say, "With all of my*

heart, I would wish Bob back tomorrow. But, given that he did die, because of what I have experienced, I am a much stronger woman, more sure of myself, than I would ever have been without this crisis. I found out there was a whole other me."

If you decide to discover new parts of you, hopefully it will be without trauma. You can start small. Would the new you wear the same clothing? How about trying just a bit more colorful scarf?

Do a random act of kindness

❦ *I had been ill for months. More so following my third and major surgery in 6 months. My husband had also been seriously ill following a major surgery that had resulted in life-threatening complications. To say the least, we were both down a pint. We were living in a new community and knew only a few people. One morning, while we were both doing the post operative shuffle, we passed the picture window and caught a glimpse of four container flower gardens on our walkway placed there by, we assumed, our new acquaintances. It felt like a turning point. The future did have good things in it. I hadn't felt like journaling for weeks, and suddenly I wanted to record this sense of joy that had returned after being taxed so heavily.*

The neighbors still won't say exactly whose idea it was, but the incident has led us to getting involved in a project called "Communities in Bloom." The little village we live near has twice been selected as the prettiest little town in Alberta, and last year we won the prettiest town in Canada for our flowers.

When you are ill it is very easy to become preoccupied with your own life. Your aches, your pains, your doctors, your disappointments, your diet, your drugs, your setbacks. It is not a character flaw. It just happens. It is an occupational hazard of being ill. It is also easy to focus on what others are doing to us or not doing for us. Turn the tables. Think about what *you* could do for someone else.

A random act of kindness changes the future. It tells us in a positive way that the future is not totally predictable. Although kindness has been around a long time, the well known book *Random Acts of Kindness*[124] has popularized the idea of being more intentional about practicing kind acts. A random act of kindness changes the past and the future. When we look back we have a refreshing memory that offsets the memories of all the difficulties we have faced. Then, when we look ahead, we understand good things can happen.

Begin with something simple. Exhausting yourself by doing a random act of kindness is not the idea. There are many simple things you can do depending on your energy or resources. Many are possible without spending any funds.

Write a note and have it hand delivered to Martin. Scent it.

Put together a little care package of goodies for Gary. They needn't be homemade.

Give Claire a small gift, and include:

some seeds, a candle or

some homemade cookies.

Do an errand that Teri was expecting to have to do.

Weed Pat's flower garden.

Visit an elderly shut-in.

Collect grocery coupons for a needy person.

Give Chris a copy of Random Acts of Kindness.

Take little steps

Rick Hansen made a trip around the world in a wheelchair. When he was asked how he did it, he replied, "One stroke at a time." Likewise, getting well or getting as well as possible is a big task. It helps to break it down. Take little steps.

When a child is learning to walk, we don't say, "For pete's sake, why don't you just get out of your crib and stride over here!" We understand that to begin with they are helpless; then they crawl, they wobble and jog with amazement at their own progress; then they pick up a toy and walk with it as if it is supporting them; then they walk, and then they run. Could you be as gentle with yourself as you are with a child? Take little steps. Keep your expectations low. Trying to do too much can actually set you back.

Remember the movie, *What About Bob?* His psychiatrist wrote a book called *Baby Steps* that helped Bob to surmount his fears by taking small steps, i.e., baby steps, toward accomplishing larger tasks. It may seem to take longer, but it works. Bob isn't the only one who finds small steps the way to go. An extensive study of women in counseling reported that a large part of their satisfaction in therapy related to help in breaking their problems into smaller parts.[125]

It is essential to have goals, perhaps even to have goals that others may think are unrealistic. A sure way to get discouraged is to want them to have happened yesterday. Impatience breeds discouragement. Whatever your goal, ask the question, "What is the smallest step towards that future that I can take today?" Over time, all of the todays will add up. If baby steps aren't getting you there, is it possible you need to be going somewhere else?

Make a wish list and begin

Adventures are best lived <u>today</u>.

Life is happening while we are getting ready for it to start! What would you like to experience?

This is a wish list, not a realistic list. You can wish for a few things that may not happen. Unless you put them on your wish list, though, you will not think about doing them. If you want a cruise, you might find you are willing to go river rafting instead. Wish lists don't have to be filled with amazing things. A wish list means there is a reason for getting up this morning. There is something to look forward to in life even if it isn't going to happen today, something worth tolerating the hassles of being unwell. Try creating a wish list.

I would like to:

- See Alaska.

- Watch my son graduate.

- Learn to bake bread.

- Read some of the classics.

- Have one meal where I didn't have to take medication.

- Have one meal out where I don't worry about how expensive it is.

- Learn to play the piano.

- Sing in public.

- Have a family photo taken.

- Run a marathon—lots of cardiac patients do.

- Become a superb photographer.

You could start by:

- Sending for a travelogue.

- Telling your son how much you hope he will graduate.

- Having a friend over to demonstrate bread making.

- Choosing one classic and beginning the first chapter.

- Putting your shoes on, going out the door and starting your training program with a one-block walk; tomorrow go one-and-a-half blocks.

- Joining a camera club. Don't even buy the camera yet.

Keep that wish list near by.

Consider becoming eccentric

Eccentrics don't worry about what is acceptable. They are characterized by a sense of humor, creative imagination and are often engrossed in a hobby. They live five to ten years longer than average with higher levels of health. [126]

I once asked a group of women to share what were the craziest things they had ever done. After hesitating initially, the women shared experience after experience, which ranged from variations on the everyday to complete lifestyle changes. At one point a woman arose and said, "I have never thought about it, but I don't think I have ever done anything crazy. I know now I have missed something. I can hardly wait to catch up!"

Have you been in a rut? Try something totally different for you. Only a few rules:

- It must not compromise your health.
- It must not hurt someone else's feelings.
- You can withdraw at any time and return to your conventional self.
- It must be something you will not regret tomorrow.

How about these?

Wear a wig.

Go down to the river and scream.

Write a letter with your non-writing hand.

Go to a rock concert.

Get up and sing karaoke.

Buy slippers with animals on the front—and wear them.

Go to the airport and take the next plane out. (For the financially well-off only!)

Wear your clothes backwards for a day. Best it's not a day when you have to go out in public.

Write Santa in July and mail it.

Take soap and draw on your windows.

Crack open an egg, scramble it and say, "There you unlucky little chicky. I am going to eat you!"

**We have assertiveness training;
...why not absurdiveness training?**

Make a memory

I was somewhat taken aback in a workshop one day when a nurse explained that over the years she had come to realize that eventually all you have is an afghan, a wheelchair and a toothbrush—and your memories.

Memories are not a substitute for living. They are, however, a record of living. What is it that we remember? We have a choice of which memories to underscore. We can recall the special times, the treasured moments, the adventures, the surprises. Or we can recall the hurts, the bad times, the resentments. Our choice.

Some memories happen by chance. We can just happen to be on the same highway as the Grand Canyon. We can happen upon a wonderful restaurant. The sunset can be magnificent at the lake shore one day. It only takes the willingness to *notice* to make those memories.

Other memories need to be created. I recall being at the bedside of a not-so-elderly man who knew he was in the last days of his life. He said, "I have no regrets. I have wonderful memories. One of the most wonderful is the day I phoned in sick and took my grandson fishing. I will never forget that day."

For the 10th anniversary of my husband Allen's major heart attack, we had a surprise "It's a matter of heart" party. We nearly gave him another heart attack when he walked in. Over the years, partially prompted by our health, we have made a habit of "makin' memories." These are intentional decisions to do something that we will later be able to recall as a memory.

Sometimes they take planning. Sometimes they are no more than being intentional about what we are doing. Here's a simple example.

During the last episode from which Allen was recovering, I inquired one day when he was obviously struggling whether it would help to "make a memory." He replied with his gentle smile, "Yeah, maybe it would."

I inquired if he had any ideas. He said, "I would love to have a hamburger."

So a hamburger it was! This would be our first excursion out. First the pillow to protect his incision and to ensure he could survive the "giggle test." That's the first few laughs after major surgery. Then the slow shuffle to the stairs and the triumph of those three steps down. A wrestle to get the safety belt on, and we were on our way. It couldn't be a chain restaurant hamburger. We went to Huckleberry's. The only homemade, pure beef patty in our nearby town. And we were served! No line-ups.

Here we were on a Friday noon. Allen was enjoying the first version of real food in weeks, the sun was shining through the window, and country music was playing quietly. It was a celebration of being alive. A small memory perhaps, but, for us, special one.

What small memory could you make today?

Take a risk

There are lots of reasons why you shouldn't do things. They might tire you out. They might not work out. They could be boring. They might be dangerous. Either way, they are a memory. How many times are our best memories something that didn't turn out or something that wasn't so great at the time?

- ❦ *We looked forward to dining with Norm and Isabel. They had selected a wonderful restaurant on an old estate. The laughter of old friendship was momentarily interrupted when the bill came. It seems we had misunderstood the menu with regard to the hors d'oeuvres. The appetizers were $9.00 per person, not just $9.00. We had added an unexpected $27.00 to our bill with a few nibblies to start off the evening!! On our incomes, it took our breath away. To this day it remains a favorite memory of eating out with our friends.*

- ❦ *John was a theater buff. Joan never had been. A few extra dollars came into the family along with the opportunity for John to go to England with a friend who loved drama. When first approached he said, "But what about my fatigue?" And fatigued he was. By all conventional standards he was not in good shape for a trip. He had been on long term disability for a chronic condition that had taken a substantive toll on his energy. Within seconds, though, a smile crept across his face. He puffed up his*

pillows, leaned forward and said, "Tired here. Tired there.
Why not?" On his trip he was often tucked into bed shortly
after supper. He returned home with a chest cold from the
February mists of England. Small compromises for seeing
"Les Miserables" in London!

Sometimes to make memories we have to be willing to take a risk. It needn't be enormous. Start small by doing something out of sequence. Or call a friend and ask them to do something with you. Have tea—real tea with a tea cozy and crumpets and thick cream. Or share the photographs of your grandson's sixth birthday with a stranger. You can try something you know you will not be good at, or eat wherever the best coupon discount is. Go on an old fashioned picnic. Invite someone over. Sit on a park bench in the freshly-fallen snow. Whatever it is, it will be memorable because you had to take a little risk.

Preserve the memories

When something special occurs, we think we will remember it forever. However, memory is not as permanent as we might imagine. Just think of how many versions of the family reunion are told a few years later. Couples may find themselves bickering about when they first met. Parents disagree when their child took his first steps. Too many ordinary—yet special— moments simply slip away, unrecorded and unremembered.

When we find we are outside of the mainstream of life for some reason, concrete memories help us to relive the good times, and help us to believe that good times can still happen. Memories are important not just for the person who lived them, but as a part of the story of those who follow. Through our memories, we pass on a history to the next generation.

You needn't be a historian or a pack rat. Simply begin to be attentive to the moments in your life that are worthy of being preserved as memory. Whether you are organized or whether you simply pile items together in a large shoe box, there will be a day when you are grateful you preserved the memories.

Save those cards.

Tell those stories to others.

Have that scrap book.

Keep that journal.

Buy those knick-knacks when you travel.

Take the camera.

Frame that picture.

Video that holiday.

Write that book.

Savor those moments.

Have a "feel good" wall.

Create a new vision

❦ *It had been a difficult year. Three surgeries in eight months. I guess it showed. Kathy was driving me to the airport. I had been in Calgary for a committee meeting—a committee from which I planned to resign. I just didn't have the energy for the extras. Kathy's wonderful vivaciousness was in contrast to my modest vitality. We often talked about life. She is just one of those people you can level with. She astutely observed, "There seems to be a sadness about you that I have never noticed before."*

My silence told me she had hit a cord. I replied, "You may be right."

Kathy pursued, "Do you have any sense of what you might be grieving?"

The words came quickly and uncensored into my mind. After a moment, I looked at her with puzzlement and shared, "This sounds crazy, but can you grieve your future?"

You *can* grieve your future. In that moment I realized that until recently I thought I knew basically what the next 15 years of my life would be like, including where I would be, what I would be doing, who I would be working with and for. Yet, at some level I knew that was now unlikely.

Only when I realized I had been unwilling to let go of the anticipated future was I able to begin to think about a new vision and version of the future. You may need to do this, too. It is not a one-day task. It will take some time. It will take facing some tough issues. At least, though, it is the right task. I needed to mourn the future I couldn't have before I was able to create the future I would have.

- Who were you in the future you thought you would have?

- How have things changed? What has not changed? What is still part of your life?

- What is non-negotiable about the future?

- What could be an unexpected bonus?

Life is a novel. You are the author, or at least the co-author. What's the theme of the next chapter?

Look at your life as a work of art

*Is there not a certain satisfaction in the fact that natural
limits are set to the life of the individual, so that at its
conclusion it may appear as a work of art?*
—Albert Einstein[127]

Your life, a work of art? Why not?

If someone were to portray your life as a work of art, what art form
would it take? Would it be a painting? A quilt? A sculpture? A piece of
music? A piece of literature? A poem, perhaps?

If a painting, would you expect bold strokes with a wide brush, or gentle
strokes with pastel colors? Would your life be a mural on the side of a
building, or more like the art of an oriental woman who paints on a kernel
of rice? If a quilt, would it be a selected pattern or a unique design? A wall
hanging or a bedcover? If a sculpture, of what material—wood, clay or
metal? If a piece of music, would it be a solo piece or written for an entire
orchestra? Which instrument would dominate? If a poem, would it be
iambic pentameter or free verse?

The artist is not always satisfied with a piece of art but recognizes it as
a work in progress. You are also a work of art in progress. Even now as you
struggle with things, what is being crafted in you?

> ❦ *Seven-year-old Robbie and his family visited the west
> coast. He was very impressed with the Cathedral Forest.
> When asked to describe the forest, Robbie said that there
> were very large trees and he meant "really, really" big
> trees. Then there were littler trees underneath them and*

there were plants and even flowers—little purple ones that his mom liked. When asked what he had learned from going there, he launched into a rather philosophical tone for such a young man. His wisdom poured out: "I learned that when you are born you don't know if you will be a big tree or a little flower. I know now. I am a little flower." Only weeks later he died of the lymphoma he had fought valiantly for two years.

Life will end. Death is not the tragedy. The tragedy is a life that has not been lived.

What small thing could you do today that would put one more stroke on the canvas of your life?

Reflections on Living in the Present

- ♥ *What's good about today?*

- ♥ *What are you going to do at least once a day to remind yourself it is good just to be alive?*

- ♥ *What's your favorite "yes, but?"*

- ♥ *Is that hobby going to be an old one or a completely new one?*

- ♥ *How much does a library card cost?*

- ♥ *Who do you know who does interesting volunteer work?*

- ♥ *What's so great about our old self?*

- ♥ *For whom would you like to do a random act of kindness?*

- ♥ *Towards what goal do you want to take a little step? Which step will it be?*

- ♥ *Which things on your wish list could you do a version of?*

- ♥ *Are you going to tell anyone about the absurd thing you are going to try?*

- ♥ *What would you really like to risk doing?*

- ♥ *Has you camera got film in it?*

- ♥ *With whom could you share your new vision of yourself?*

- ♥ *What art form would most represent your life?*

Postscript

*A*s Allen and I sat savoring a homemade bean soup during a break in the editing process of this book, the furrows in his forehead announced the fatigue that entering the corrections into the computer seemed to bring on.

"The fatigue," he shared, "takes away some of the enjoyment."

I nodded with a confirming glance, replying, "There are all of the options in the book, but sometimes ya' just feel punk."

On those days, be gentle with yourself. Keep the expectations reasonable. Hope is that voice inside whispering, "Yes, I can. If not today, perhaps tomorrow."

To repeat the words of the introduction:

> ***There is no panacea. There is no recipe.***
> ***We hope. We cope. On occasion, we mope.***
>
> ***We need all three.***

Recommended Reading

Bombeck, Erma: *I Want to Grow Hair, I Want to Grow Up, I Want to Go to Boise: Children Surviving Cancer*. New York: Harper, 1989.

Branden, Nathanial: *The Power of Self-Esteem*. Florida: Health Communications, Inc., 1992.

Bressler, David: *Free Yourself from Pain*. New York: Simon & Schuster, Inc., 1979.

Bridges, William: *Managing Transition: Making the Most of Change*. New York: Addison-Wesley, 1991.

Burns, David: *Feeling Good: The New Mood Therapy*. New York: Penguin, 1981.

Callwood, June: *Emotions:What They Are and How They Affect Us*. New York: Doubleday, 1986.

Chopra, Deepak: *Quantum Healing: Exploring the Frontiers of Mind/Body Medicine*. New York: Bantam, 1989.

Colgrove, Melba, Harold Bloomfield and Peter McWilliams: *How to Survive the Loss of a Love*. Los Angeles: Prelude Press, 1991.

Cosby, Bill: *Love and Marriage*. New York: Doubleday, 1990.

Cousins, Norman: *Anatomy of an Illness As Perceived by the Patient*. New York: Bantam, 1979.

Dyer, Wayne: *You'll See it When You Believe It*. New York: Avon, 1989.

Dyer, Wayne: *Your Erroneous Zones*. New York: Avon, 1976.

Fenwick, Catherine Ripplinger: *Healing with Humour: A First Aid Kit.* Muenster, Sask.: St. Peter's Press, 1995.

Frankl, Viktor: *Man's Search for Meaning.* New York: Washington Square Press, 1966.

Glasser, William: *Positive Addiction.* Kansas City, MO: Andrews McMeel, 1985.

Greenburg, Dan and Marcia Jacobs: *How to Make Yourself Miserable for the Rest of the Century.* New York: Random, 1986.

Greenwood, Micheal and Peter Nunn: *Paradox and Healing: Medicine, Mythology and Transformation..* Victoria, B.C.: Meridian, 1992.

Hafen, Brent, Keith Karren, Kathryn Frandsen, and N. Lee Smith: *Mind/Body Health: The Effects of Attitude Emotions and Relationships.* Needham Heights, MA: Allyn & Bacon, 1995.

Hanson, Peter: *The Joy of Stress.* Kansas City, MO: Andrews McMeel, 1985.

Jevne, Ronna Fay: *It All Begins with Hope: Patients, Caregivers and the Bereaved Speak Out.* San Diego, CA: Lura Media, 1991.

Jevne, Ronna Fay: *The Voice of Hope: Heard Across the Heart of Life.* San Diego, CA: Lura Media, 1994.

Jevne, Ronna and Alexander Levitan: *No Time for Nonsense: Self-Help for the Seriously Ill.* San Diego, CA: Lura Media, 1989.

Jevne, Ronna and James Miller: *Finding Hope: Ways of Seeing Life in a Brighter Light.* Ft. Wayne, IN: Willowgreen Publishing, 1999.

Jevne, Ronna and Donna Reilly Williams: *When Dreams Don't Work: Professional Caregivers and Burnout.* Amityville, NY: Baywood Publishing, 1998.

Kushner, Harold: *When Bad Things Happen to Good People.* New York: Avon, 1981.

Levine, Stephen: *Meetings at the Edge.* Toronto: Doubleday, 1984.

Levine, Stephen: *Healing Into Life and Death*. Toronto: Doubleday, 1987.

Lewis, C.S.: *Surprised by Joy: The Shape of My Early Life*. New York: Harcourt, 1955.

Lewis, C.S.: *The Problem of Pain*. Glasgow: Collins, 1940.

LeShan, Lawrence: *You Can Fight for Your Life: Emotional Factors in the Causation of Cancer*. New York: M. Evans & Co., 1977.

London, Oscar: *Kill as Few Patients as Possible and Fifty-six Other Essays on How to be the World's Best Doctor*. Berkeley CA: Ten Speed Press, 1987.

Mitchell, Jann: *Codependent for Sure*. Kansas City, MO: Andrews McMeel, 1992.

Moyers, Bill: *Healing and the Mind*. New York: Doubleday, 1993.

Powell, John: *A Reason to Live! A Reason to Die!* Illinois: Argus, 1975.

Prather, Hugh: *Notes to Myself*. New York: Bantam, 1970.

Sheehy, Gail: *Passages: Predictable Crises of Adult Life*. New York: Dutton, 1974.

Siegel, Bernie: *Love, Medicine and Miracles: Lessons Learned about Self-Healing from a Surgeon's Experience with Exceptional Patients*. New York: Harper, 1986.

Siegel, Bernie: *Peace, Love and Healing: Bodymind Communication and the Path to Self-Healing: An Exploration*. New York: Harper, 1989.

Stettbacher, J. Konrad: *Making Sense of Suffering: The Healing Confrontation with Your Past*. New York: Dutton, 1991.

Stock, Gregory: *The Kid's Book of Questions*. New York: Workman, 1988.

Triere, Lynette, with Richard Peacock: *Learning to Leave: A Woman's Guide*. New York: Warner, 1982.

von Oech, Roger: *A Whack on the Side of the Head: How You Can Be More Creative.* New York: Warner, 1990.

Watzlawick, Paul: *The Situation Is Hopeless, but Not Serious (The Pursuit of Unhappiness).* New York: Norton, 1993.

Notes

1. Jevne, R.: *It All Begins with Hope: Patients, Caregivers and the Bereaved Speak Out.* San Diego, CA: Lura Media, 1991, p. 9.

2. Jevne, R.: *The Voice of Hope Heard Across the Heart of Life.* San Diego, CA: Lura Media, 1994, p. 8.

3. Edey, W.: "Hoping and coping: the almost identical twins," *Hope News,* 7(3), June 1998, p. 3.

4. Frankl, V.: *Man's Search for Meaning.* New York: Washington Square Press, 1963, p. 104.

5. Wendy Edey, personal correspondence, November, 1997.

6. Gershen Kaufman, as quoted in: *The Psychology of Shame: Theory and Treatment of Shame-Based Syndromes.* New York: Springer Publishing, 1989, p. 46. Suggests three messages inherent in our society that encourage shame: compete to be successful, be independent and self-sufficient, and be popular and conform. If we are powerless to live up to these messages, we are vulnerable to shame.

7. Mufty Mathewson, personal correspondence, 1992.

8. Hope House is the home of the Hope Foundation of Alberta, whose mission it is to enhance hope through research, education and service. It is affiliated with the University of Alberta, Edmonton, Alberta, Canada.

9. Credit goes to Wendy Edey, Hope House's in-house chartered psychologist who seems to have endless creative ways of thinking about the human condition.

10. O'Regan, B. and C. Hirshberg: *Spontaneous Remission: An Annotated Bibliography.* Sausalito, CA: Institute of Noetic Sciences, 1995, p. xiii.

11. Thomas, L.: *The Youngest Science: Notes of a Medicine Watcher.* New York: Viking Press, 1983, p. 205.

12. O'Regan and Hirshberg. This book provides extensive documentation of the phenomena of spontaneous remission. Cancer is the most commonly researched condition with regard to spontaneous remission, but the phenomenon occurs across a broad spectrum of disease. Between 1966 and October 1992 in the Medline database there have been 10,603 appearances of the terms "spontaneous remission" or "spontaneous regression." The Remission Project of the Institute of Noetic Sciences searched the world's medical literature and assembled a data base of medically reported cases of spontaneous remission of more than 3,500 references from more than 800 journals in 20 different languages.

13. Ornstein, R. and D. Sobel: *The Healing Brain: Breakthrough Discoveries About How the Brain Keeps Us Healthy.* New York: Simon and Schuster, 1987, pp. 18-23. Credit for the repeal of illnesses is commonly wrongly attributed to advances in medicine. For example, 97 percent of tuberculosis cases had already been eliminated by the time streptomycin was introduced in 1947. By the time immunization had occurred, 90 percent of whooping cough had disappeared. Safer water, better sewage disposal, pasteurization of milk and more careful preparation of food likely deserve the credit.

14. De Pressensé, E.: *The Mystery of Suffering and Other Discourse.* London: Hodder & Stoughton, 1868, p. 16.

15. Lorraine Dahlberg, personal communication: *THE GAP-Commentary.* The "GAP" is a piece of artwork completed in 1994.

16. Cousins, N.: *Head First: The Biology of Hope and the Healing Power of the Human Spirit.* New York: E.P. Dutton, 1989.

17. Dreher, H.: "Cancer and the mind: current concepts in psycho-oncology." *Advances*, 4(3): 1987, pp. 27-43.

18. Peterson, C. and L. Bossio: *Health and Optimism.* New York: The Free Press, 1991.

19. Peterson C., G. Vaillant, and M. Seligman: "Pessimistic explanatory style is a risk factor for physical illness: a thirty-five year longitudinal study." *Journal of Personality and Social Psychology*, 55(1): 1988.

20. Ranard, A.: "The world through rose-colored glasses." *Health*, August 1989, p. 58.

21. Seligman, M.: *Learned Optimism.* New York: Alfred Knopf, 1991.

22. Silver, N.: "Do optimists live longer?" *American Health*, November, 1986, pp. 50-53.

23. Williams, P. and J. Roger: *You Can't Afford the Luxury of a Negative Thought.* Los Angeles, CA: Prelude Press, 1987, p. 133.

24. Studies of cardiac patients suggest that social support is a key factor in cardiovascular health. For example: K. Orth-Gomer and A. Unden: "Type A behavior, social support and coronary risk: interaction and significance for mortality in cardiac patients." *Psychosomatic Medicine*, 52 (1): 1990, pp. 59-72. J. Kilik, and H. Mahler: "Social support and recovery from surgery." *Health Psychology*, 8 (2): 1989, pp. 221-238; R. Chacko, R. Harper, J. Gotto, J. Young: "Psychiatric interview and psychometric predictors of cardiac transplant survival." *American Journal of Psychiatry*, 53 (12): 1996, pp. 1607-1612; P. Farmer, P. Meyer, D. Ramsey, D. Goff, and M. Wear: "Higher levels of social support predict greater survival following acute myocardial infarction: The Corpus Christi Heart Project." *Behavior Medicine*, 22 (2): 1996, pp. 59-66; G. Invernizzi, C. Bressi, P. Bertrando, A. Passerini, *et al.*: "Emotional profiles of families with a heart-operated patient: a pilot study." *Psychotherapy & Psychosomatics*, 55 (1): 1991, pp. 1-8. All

of these studies confirm a similar phenomena in patients and families experiencing cancer.

25. Kast, V.: *Joy, Inspiration and Hope.* College Station, TX: Texas A&M University Press, 1991, p. 12.

26. Carola, R., J. Harley, and C. Noback: *Human Anatomy and Physiology.* New York: McGraw-Hill, 1990, pp. 73-77.

27. Konnick, J.: "Sleep, the common denominator for psychological adaptation." *Canadian Psychology,* 38(3): 1997, pp. 191-195.

28. Evans, J. and D. French: "Sleep and healing in intensive care settings." *Dimensions of Critical Care Nursing,* 14 (4): 1995, pp. 189-198.

29. Jeffrey, R. and S. French: "Epidemic obesity in the United States: are fast foods and television viewing contributing?" *American Journal of Public Health,* 88 (2): 1998, pp. 277-280.

30. Grodstein, F., R. Levine, L. Troy, T. Spencer, G. Colditz, and M. Stampfer: "Three-year follow-up of participants in a commercial weight loss program. Can you keep it off?" *Archives of Internal Medicine,* 156 (12): 1996, pp. 1302-6.

31. Tara, H. and M. Gage: "Advertised foods on children's television." *Archives of Pediatrics & Adolescent Medicine,* 149 (6): 1995, pp. 649-52.

32. Tiggeman, M.: "Dietary restraint as a predictor of reported weight loss and affect." *Psychological Reports,* 75 (3 pt. 2): 1994, pp. 1679-82.

33. McCargar, L., J. Sale, and S. Crawford: "Chronic dieting does not result in a sustained reduction in resting metabolic rate in overweight women." *Journal of the American Dietetic Association,* 96 (11): 1996, pp. 1175-7.

34. Skender, M., G. Goodrick, D. Del Junco, R. Reeves, L. Darnell, A. Gotto, and J. Foreyt: "Comparison of 2-year weight loss trends in behavioral treatments of obesity: diet, exercise and combination

interventions." *Journal of American Dietetic Association*, 96 (4): 1996, pp. 342-46.

35. Colt, G. H.: "The magic of touch." *Life*, August: 1997, pp. 53-62

36. Touch Research Institute, Department of Pediatrics, University of Miami School of Medicine. Contact: P.O. Box 016820, 1601 NW 12th Avenue, Miami, FL 33101.

37. Colt, pp. 53-62.

38. Gray, K. B.: "A man's best friend." *Nursing Times*. 84(34): 1988, pp. 40-44.

39. Hoelscher, K. and T. Garfat: "Talking to the animal." *Journal of Child and Youth Care*, 8(3): (1993), pp. 8-92.

40. Clark, E.: *Growing Old is Not for Sissies II: Portraits of Senior Athletes*. San Francisco: Pomegranate Artbooks, 1995.

41. Numerous ideas from "Good Humor, Good Health." *Mind/Body Newsletter*, 6(1): 1997, p. 3, are used in this section.

42. Rutherford, A.: "A natural balance." *Harrowsmith*, 1994, pp. 62-68.

43. Korsh, B. and C. Harding: *The Intelligent Patient's Guide to the Doctor-Patient Relationship: Learning How to Talk so Your Doctor Will Listen*. New York: Oxford University, 1997.

44. Cohen, L. J.: "Phenomenology of therapeutic reading with implications for research and practice of bibliotherapy." *Arts in Psychotherapy*, 21(1): 1994, pp. 37-44.

45. Landreville, P.: "Cognitive bibliotherapy for depression in older adults with a disability." *Clinical Gerontologist*, 19(3): 1998, pp. 69-75.

46. Mimeault, V. and C. M. Morin: "Self-help treatment for insomnia: bibliotherapy with and without professional guidance." *Journal of Consulting & Clinical Psychology*, 67: 1999, pp. 511-519.

47. Hirshberg, C. and M. Barasch: *Remarkable Recovery: What Extraordinary Healings Can Tell Us about Getting Well.* New York: Riverhead Books, 1995.

48. Shorter, E.: *A History of Psychiatry from the Era of the Asylum to the Age of Prozac.* New York: John Wiley & Sons, 1997, p. 21.

49. Thom, D. and B. Campbell: "Patient-physician trust: an exploratory study." *The Journal of Family Practice*, 44 (2): 1997, p. 171.

50. Wylie-Wong, G. and R. Jevne: "Patient Hope: Exploring the interactions between physicians and HIV seropositive individuals." *Qualitative Health Research*, 7(1): 1997, pp. 32-56.

51. Adapted from: "Rx self care tips," *Mind/Body Health Newsletter*, 1(1): 1997, p. 7.

52. Coambs, R., P. Jensen, M. Hoa Her, B. Ferguson, J. Jarry, J. Wong, and R. Abrahamsohn: *Review of the Scientific Literature on the the Prevalence, Consequences, Health Costs of Noncompliance and Inappropriate Use of Prescription Medication in Canada.* Ottawa: University of Toronto Press, 1995.

53. Eisenberg, D., R. Kessler, C. Foster, F. Norlock, D. Calkins, and T. Delbanco: "Unconventional medicine in the United States: prevalence, costs and patterns of use." *The New England Journal of Medicine*, 328(4): 1993, pp. 246-252.

54. Kaegi, E. and Canadian Cancer Society (Ontario Division): "A patient's guide to unconventional therapies." *Canadian Medical Association Journal*, 158 (9): 1998, pp. 1161-1165.

55. Dossey, L.: *Healing Words: The Power of Prayer and the Practice of Medicine.* New York: HarperCollins, 1993, p. 17.

56. Jevne, R., D. Ryan, and A. Eng: *Health, Hope and Taking Charge.* Edmonton, Alberta: Hope Foundation of Alberta, 1998.

57. "Loneliness and health" in B. Hafen, K. Frandsen, K. Karren, and K. Hooker: *The Health Effects of Attitude, Emotion, Relationships.* Provo, Utah: EMS Associates, 1992, pp. 283-309. This chapter

provides an excellent summary of the health risks of loneliness and the benefits of friendship.

58. From W. Shakespeare: *The Tragedy of Romeo and Juliet.* Act II, scene 2.

59. Moore, T.: *Care of the Soul: A Guide for Cultivating Depth and Sacredness in Everyday Life.* New York: HarperCollins, 1992, p. 237.

60. Baur, S.: *Confiding: A Psychotherapist and Her Patients Search for Stories to Live By.* New York: HarperCollins, 1994.

61. Pennebaker, J.: *Opening Up: The Healing Power of Confiding in Others.* New York: William Morrow, 1990.

62. Skubik, S.: "Body, Mind, and Soul: An Interview with Nancy Mairs." *World Magazine*, Sep/Oct: 1997, p. 16.

63. At Hope House, people are encouraged to talk about what enhances and threatens hope. Sometimes this involves symptoms specific to their condition, but just as often does not.

64. Boisvert, J. : "The experience of hope in a support group for persons with eating disorders." Unpublished paper: Hope Foundation of Alberta, 1999.

65. Ludtke, M.: "Can the mind help cure disease?" *Time*, March 12, 1990, p. 76. Effects on mood, coping, symptoms and survival are now documented through many excellently designed studies.

66. Hildingh, C., B. Fridlund, and K. Segesten, "Social support in self-help groups, as experienced by persons having coronary heart disease and their next of kin." *International Journal of Nursing Studies*, 32(3): 1995, pp. 224-232.

67. Oxman, T., D. Freeman, and E. Manheimer: "Lack of social participation or religious strength and comfort as risk factors for death after cardiac surgery in the elderly." *Psychosomatic Medicine*, 57 (1): 1995, pp. 5-15.

68. For more about negaholics, read C. Carter-Scott: *Negaholics: How to Recover from Your Addiction to Negativity and Turn Your Life Around.* New York: Villard Books, 1989.

69. Hinsz, V. and J. Tomhave: "Smile and (half) the world smiles with you, frown and you frown alone." *Personality and Social Psychology Bulletin*, 17(5): 1991, pp. 586-592.

70. Friedrich Nietzsche, as quoted in L. Leshan: "The world of the patient in severe pain of long duration." *Journal of Chronic Disease*, 17: 1964, pp. 119-126.

71. Jeffers, S.: *Feel and Fear and Do it Anyway.* New York: Fawcett Columbine, 1987.

72. Ferch, S.: "Intentional forgiving as a counseling intervention." *Journal of Counseling and Development*, vol. 76, pp. 261-270.

73. Hafen, B., K. Frandsen, K. Karren, N. L. Smith: *Mind/Body Health: The Effects of Attitude, Emotions, and Relationships.* Needham Heights, MA: Allyn & Bacon, 1995, p. 169.

74. "Anger and health" (pp. 169-180) and "Hostility and health" (pp. 181-202) in: B. Hafen, K. Frandsen, K. Karren , and K. Hooker: *The Health Effects of Attitude, Emotion, Relationships.* Provo, UT: EMS Associates, 1992.

75. There are many books that assist people to begin keeping a journal. A simple and helpful beginning is: J. E. Miller*: The Rewarding Practice of Journal Writing: A Guide for Starting and Keeping Your Personal Journal.* Fort Wayne, IN: Willowgreen Publishing, 1998.

76. Adams, K.: *The Way of the Journal: A Journal Therapy Workbook for Healing.* Lutherville, MD: The Sidran Press, 1998. This book is repleat with specific suggestions and has an excellent bibiography.

77. Lindbergh, A. M.: *Gift From the Sea.* New York: Pantheon Books, 1975, p. 118.

78. Taylor-Hough, D.: *Frozen Assets: How to Cook for a Day and Eat for a Month.* Vancouver, WA: Champion Press Ltd., 1998.

79. Wilson, M. S., M. B. Lagerborg, and M. Wilson: *Once-a-Month Cooking: A Proven System for Spending Less Time in the Kitchen & Enjoying Delicious, Homemade Meals Everyday.* Nashville, TN: Broadman & Holman, 1999.

80. Mathewson, M.: *Courage after Coma.* Edmonton, Alberta: Uneek Experience Ltd., 1997, pp. 43-44.

81. Lazarus, R. and S. Folkman: *Stress, Appraisal and Coping.* New York: Springer Publishing, 1984.

82. Ferch, S.: *Meaning of Touch in Forgiveness for Six Christians.* Unpublished doctoral dissertation, University of Alberta, Edmonton, Alberta, Canada., 1996, p. 147.

83. Foregiveness is begining to be recognized as important in the experience of illness. L. Phillips and J. Osborne: "Cancer patients' experiences of foregiveness therapy." *Canadian Journal of Counseling*, 23 (3), 1989, pp. 236-251.

84. Mermann, A. C.: "Spiritual aspects of death and dying." *Yale Journal of Biology and Medicine*, 65 (2): 1992, pp. 137-142.

85. Kaye, J. and K. Robinson: "Spirituality among caregivers." *Image-the Journal of Nursing Scholarship*, 26 (3), 1994, pp. 218-221.

86. DiBlasio, F. and B. Benda: *Practitioners, Religion and the Use of Forgiveness in the Clinical Setting*, 7, 1993, pp. 183-190.

87. Kirkup, P.: "Some religious perpectives on forgiveness and settling differences." *Mediation Quarterly*, 11 (1), 1993, pp. 79-94.

88. Donnelly, D.: *Putting Forgiveness into Practice.* Allen, Texas: Argus Communication, 1982, p. 20

89. Deepak Chopra, in: B. Janes, (Producer), J. Torrance, (Producer), and H. Schuurman, (Director). *The Healing Spirit* [film], 1993. (Available from National Film Board, Constitution Square, 360 Albert Street, Suite 1560, Ottawa Ontraio, K1A 0M9).

90. Lynch, W.: *Images of Hope: Imagination as Healer of the Hopeless.* New York: The New American Library, 1965, p. 108.

91. Cousineau, P.: *Soul: An Archeology.* San Francisco: HarperCollins, 1994, p. xxvi.

92. Moore, p. 4.

93. Moir Messervy, J.: *The Inward Garden: Creating a Place of Beauty and Meaning.* Toronto, Canada: Little Brown & Company, 1995, p. 19.

94. Simson, S. and M. Straus (eds.): *Horticulture as Therapy: Principles and Practices.* New York: Food Book Press/Haworth Press, 1997.

95. McGuire, D.: "Implementing horticultural therapy into a geriatric long term care facility." *Activities, Adaptation and Aging.* vol 22(1-2), 1997, pp. 61-80.

96. Burgess, C.: "Horticulture and its application to institutionalized elderly." *Activities, Adaptation and Aging* vol. 14(3), 1990, pp. 51-61.

97. Hewson, M.: *Horticulture as Therapy: A Practical Guide to Using Horticulture as a Therapeutic Tool.* Ravensdale, WA: Idyll Arbor, 1998.

98. Smith, D.: "Alleviating stress for caregivers of frail elders using horticultural therapy." *Activities, Adaptation and Aging.* Vol. 22 (1-2), pp. 93-105.

99. Noyles, R.: *English Romantic Poetry and Prose.* NewYork: Oxford University Press, 1956, p. 310.

100. Dossey, p. 89.

101. Nouwen, H.: *With Open Hands.* Notre Dame, IN: Ava Maria Press, 1995, p. 61.

102. Lewis, C.S.: *Letters to Malcolm: Chiefly on Prayer.* New York: Harcourt, Brace & World, 1964, p. 63.

103. Dossey, p. 18.

104. Foster, R. J.: *Prayer: Finding the Heart's True Home*. San Francisco: HarperCollins, 1992, p. vii.

105. Skubik, p. 15.

106. Cooper, D.: *The Heart of Stillness: The Elements of Spiritual Practice*. New York: Bell Tower, 1992.

107. Jevne, R. F. and A. Levitan: *No Time for Nonsense: Getting Well Against the Odds*. San Diego, CA: Lura Media, 1989, pp. 174-179.

108. Campbell, J., B.S. Flowers, (Ed.), with B. Moyers (contr.): *The Power of Myth*. New York: Doubleday, 1988, p. 216.

109. Thank you to Wendy Edey for these thoughts on music.

110. Barrineau, P.: *Memo to Cancer*. North Carolina: Heritage Printers Inc., 1991.

111. Hiebert, C.: *Gift of Wings: An Aerial Celebration of Canada*. North York, Ontario: Stoddart Publishing, 1995.

112. Csikszentmihzalyi, M.: *Flow: The Psychology of Optimal Experience*. New York: HarperCollins, 1991.

113. Canadian Ministry of Industry, Statistics. *Cat. no. 87-211*, 1995, p. 49.

114. Rane-Szostak, D. and K. Herth: "Pleasure reading, other activities and loneliness in later life." *Journal of Adolescent and Adult Literacy*, 39(2): 1995, pp. 100-108.

115. Fulghum, R.: *From Beginning to End: The Rituals of Our Lives*. New York: Ivy Books, 1996, p. 103.

116. Kohn. A.: "Do religious people help more? Not so you would notice." *Psychology Today*. December 1989, p. 66.

117. Canadian Ministry of Industry, Statistics. *Cat. no. 71-542-XPE*, 1995, p. 27.

118. Peterson and Bossio, p. 49.

119. Howard, A.: "Helping and health: the relationship between volunteer activity and health related outcomes." *Advances*, 7(1): 1990, pp. 25-34.

120. "The return of generosity." *Health*, August, 1989, p. 13.

121. Cowley, G.: "A disaster brings out the best in people. Why?" *Newsweek*, November 6, 1989, pp. 40, 44.

122. Growald, E. R. and A. Luks: "Beyond self." *American Health*, March: 1988, pp. 51-53.

123. Keegan, L.: *Healing Nutrition (Nurse as Healer).* Albany, NY: Delmar Publishers, 1996, p. 10.

124. Conari Press Editors: *Random Acts of Kindness.* Berkeley, CA: Conari Press, 1993.

125. Talley, J. T. Butcher, and J. Moorman: *The Predictors of Successful Very Brief Psychotherapy: A Study of Differences by Gender, Age, and Treatment Variables.* Springfield, IL: Thomas. C.C., 1992.

126. Weeks, D.: *Eccentrics: The Scientific Investigation.* Edinburgh, Scotland: Sterling University Press, L27-50. (Royal Edinburgh Hospital, Morningshide Terrace, Edinburgh, 1988).

127. Burke, T. (ed.): *Einstein A Portrait.* Corte Madera, CA: Pomegranate Artbooks, 1984.

About the Author

*R*onna Jevne, Ph.D., is professor of educational psychology at the University of Alberta as well as a psychologist, lecturer and writer who is internationally known for her work in the area of hope. She is a founding member and program director of the Hope Foundation of Alberta, whose mission it is to study and enhance hope as it relates to health and to learning (*www.ualberta.ca/hope*). It has a research, education and counseling program. Dr. Jevne's passion for hope began during her time as the head of the Department of Psychology at the Cross Cancer Institute. An author of many books, monographs and articles, she enjoys combining her love of writing with her love of photography. Despite chronic health conditions, she and her husband, Allen, share a life of love and laughter.